UNDERSTANDING STRATEGIC CHANGE

A Guide for Dental Laboratory Managers

Dr. Charlie Lee

MPhil, PhD, LCGI, FETC, RDT

Foreword by

Mr. Ray Winstanley

BDS, MDS, FDS, RCS (Ed)

Published by the Dental Laboratories Association Limited 2006

For the benefit of its members (Dental Laboratory Owners) who are embarking on a period of economic and political change and uncertainty, and Dental Laboratory Managers in Dental Hospitals and Schools who are also subject to constant change.

Published by the Dental Laboratories Association Limited 2006

The Author of this work has been identified as Dr Charlie Lee.

ISBN-13: 978 0 9552329 0 9
ISBN-10: 0 9552329 0 2

Typeset, printed and bound by Q3 Digital/Litho – 01509 213456

CONTENTS

FIGURES

FOREWORD – Mr. Ray Winstanley

The dental laboratory is an essential, but often neglected, "player" in the 'dental team'. In order to flourish in the future, and thereby give essential support to the clinician and patient, laboratories must be managed effectively.

Charlie Lee has spent all his working life involved with dental laboratories. His three years as a Royal Air Force Apprentice were in dental technology, from where he went on to become a Sergeant in the Royal Air Force Dental Branch serving 13 years. He then moved to Stoke Mandeville Hospital for a period of 12 years where he held the posts of Senior, Chief, and Senior Chief Maxillo-Facial Technician before moving into dental laboratory management as Dental Laboratory Manager at the Glasgow Dental Hospital and School. Following seven years in this post, he was appointed to the posts of Dental Laboratory Manager then Operational and Technical Services Manager at the Charles Clifford Dental Hospital, Sheffield, appointments he held until early retirement in 2004.

His experience and expertise in dental technology and dental laboratory management, including the planning and implementation of strategic change, is such that he has undertaken a number of consultancies in the field of dental laboratory management, reviewing services and structure and advising where appropriate.

He has both a Masters Degree in Philosophy (MPhil) and a Doctor of Philosophy Degree (PhD) from the University of Sheffield from research carried out in this area. Such credentials place him in a unique position to offer management courses, bringing together his thoughts and ideas gained from wide study.

Any owner/manager of a dental laboratory would benefit from this book, if only to show that they are developing their company/laboratory in the best way for future needs and demands of the laboratory and its customers. Dental technicians wishing to progress into dental laboratory management would also find the theories and concepts of strategic management useful in their studies and development.

Topics include *introduction to strategy and strategic management; strategic leadership; planning and implementing change; total quality management and the customer.*

PREFACE

Strategic management is concerned with understanding, as well as choosing and implementing, the strategy or strategies that a company/dental laboratory follows. It is a complex process which can be considered from a number of different perspectives. There is no single approach, model or theory to the management of strategic change. Dental laboratory managers not only need to be skilled and experienced; they also need to be aware that the pressures to change are always present in the form of opportunities and threats and they need to respond positively. The approaches and decisions they make must ensure they are the most efficient and effective.

The aim of this book is to help dental laboratory managers understand the process of managing strategic change, develop strategic awareness and determine the issues and questions which must be addressed if changes in strategy are to be formulated and implemented effectively. The managerial and behavioural processes which take place within the laboratory, in order that they can understand how changes come about, are also discussed.

Understanding Strategic Change pieces together the author's previous studies of private sector companies and dental laboratories with the relevant literature to evaluate the theories and concepts of strategic management and implementation of change. Models provide a framework for evaluating how dental laboratory managers can reach their decisions and objectives in order to become, and remain, successful.

The book outlines that the strategic ideas and methods used by private sector companies, and these are discussed in the context of the relevant literature.

Chapter 1 provides an overview of the National Health Service

(NHS) with particular reference to NHS Trust hospitals, dentistry and dental laboratory services. Chapters 2–6 give an insight into the processes that underline strategic management, success, leadership and culture.

Chapters 7–9 show how these processes, together with the methods used in private sector companies, can be adapted to provide a framework for managing the process of strategic change in a dental laboratory.

The terminology used in the book has been kept simple in order to avoid the pitfall of jargon that management writers often fall into. **The words 'company', 'organisation', and 'business' which are used in referenced text and discussion areas should be taken as being synonymous.** The term "Dental Laboratory Manager" applies to dental technicians who are dental laboratory owners or manage a hospital laboratory.

Reference to the National Health Service (NHS) refers to England, Wales and Northern Ireland only, and does not include Scotland.

The strategic management issues addressed in the book not only apply to dental laboratory managers and technicians who manage a small department within a dental laboratory, but also to those who are seeking to move into dental laboratory management.

Key point boxes are featured separately at the end of relevant chapters for special emphasis and easy reference.

ACKNOWLEDGEMENTS

I would like to acknowledge and thank all the unnamed managers and staff in the companies and dental laboratories I visited for their contribution and co-operation with the case studies used in my research. Their experiences, the problems they have faced and how they have endeavoured to overcome them, have been instrumental in the development of this book.
My sincere thanks also go to:

The Department of Adult Dental Care, School of Clinical Dentistry, University of Sheffield, for enabling me to carry out my research.

The Charles Clifford Dental Hospital, Sheffield for granting me time to complete my case studies.

Mr Ray Winstanley for his help and advice during my research and his constructive comments during the development of the book text.

The Dental Laboratories Association, British Dental Trade Association, Nobel Biocare UK Ltd., International Dental Education Academy and Q3 Digital/Litho, for their help and support in publishing the book.

My wife Lilian for her encouragement and tolerating the long hours I spent researching and writing.

Chapter 1

INTRODUCTION

National Health Service

An overview

In the last few years the National Health Service (NHS) has had to change to an extent and at a pace which exceeded anything in its first 40 years of existence.[1] The speed at which these changes within the NHS occurred affected managers at all levels. The areas most affected were: Accountability, funding, working practices, technology, legislation (Health and Safety, and European Directives), and the competition brought about by the internal market.

The NHS reforms have sought to make managers at all levels accountable for the resources they use and a requirement to develop information systems against which performance can be measured.[2] Accountable management therefore gives managers budgets for which they are responsible and targets which they agree to meet. This is seen, on the one hand, to instill greater control and accountability over resources used in the NHS, and on the other, to have the potential to encourage managers to be entrepreneurial. That is, at least in theory, meant to imply that resource use is best determined by those at grass root level, and if savings and improved efficiencies can be made then, ideally, they might be deployed by budget holders in the ways that they think best.

In reality not *all* of this has materialised. At the end of the day the NHS remains, as it always has been, an organisation which is accountable to the Secretary of State for Health and through him or her to Parliament.

There is therefore a high degree of centralisation and control from the top despite the rhetoric over many years of devolved management and responsibility. Accountability remains firmly upwards both in respect of the purchasers and providers.

Trust Hospitals

During the early period following the creation of the internal market strategy, implementation in Trust hospitals was varied and as problematical as it was for the purchasers.[2] Many hospitals focused on operational rather than strategic planning and were more concerned about survival and winning contracts than about the strategic direction they may wish to take in the future.

Trusts were faced with difficult choices regarding the prioritisation of services. It was essential that, as new structures and working relationships developed, investment was maintained in order to develop services to a standard consistent with both public (customer) expectations and advancing technologies.

Financial constraints within which hospitals work often mean there are insufficient resources available to implement the service developments that the hospital and/or individual departments wish to make.

In 1997 the Government introduced a White Paper outlining its proposals to gradually dismantle the internal market and replace it with a more collaborative partnership based approach.[3] The proposals in the White Paper freed NHS Trusts to use their managerial and clinical expertise to concentrate on providing improved services for patients. Incentives were made available to help NHS Trusts succeed and they were backed by a tough approach to performance management in order to drive improvement in quality and efficiency.

The changes enabled NHS Trusts to retain full local responsibility for operational management so that they could make best use of resources for patient care. They did so within a local service framework that they themselves had played a significant part in creating: NHS Trusts accountable to Health Authorities and Primary Care Groups for the services they drive and the NHS Executive for their statutory duties.

In the internal market, NHS Trusts received their funding

under contracts negotiated annually. Many treatments were funded on a 'cost-per-case' or 'extra-contractual-referral' basis. The new funding arrangements meant resources being distributed fairly through Health Authorities to inclusive Primary Care groups. NHS Trusts continued to devolve budgetary responsibility to clinical teams and managers.

The vision set out in the 1997 White Paper was aimed at ensuring NHS Trusts provided a high quality and efficient service to patients while at the same time involving staff at all levels in planning change through empowerment and improved communication links. This approach to putting patients (customers) first is one that has been adopted successfully by private sector companies and will be highlighted in future chapters. NHS Trust hospitals approached this change in direction with some caution, particularly at a time when financial pressures on hospitals continued to increase year on year. Inevitably the financial position of the purchasers meant they were increasingly unable to purchase services to match demand.[4]

A system of 'clinical governance' was introduced by the Secretary of State for Health to focus on quality in NHS Trusts and ensure that quality improvement processes were in place and integrated with the quality programme for the organisation as a whole. Every NHS Trust was required to embrace this new concept so that quality was at the core, both in terms of responsibilities as organisations and of each of the staff as individual professionals.

Foundation Trust Hospitals

NHS Plan

The NHS Plan, published in July 2000, set out the Government's ambitious ten-year plan to modernise the NHS and social care system. This was supplemented by *Delivering the NHS Plan: next steps on investment, next steps on reform,* published in April 2002. It continued the journey – begun with the *NHS Plan* – towards a devolved health service, offering wider choice and greater diversity bound together by common standards, tough inspection and

NHS values. *Delivering the NHS Plan* set out proposals for developing a new type of organisation – NHS Foundation Trusts.

In July 2002, *Eligibility Criteria and Timetable* was published. The document gave an update on the development of NHS foundation trust policy and set out the timetable for the application process. Specialist and acute NHS trusts that received 3 stars in the 2001/02 NHS Performance Ratings were invited to apply for NHS Foundation Trust status.

A Guide to NHS Foundation Trusts was published in December 2002 and set out the detailed policy proposals and structure for NHS Foundation Trusts. The Guide included information about governance arrangements, constitution, licensing and provision of NHS services.

Raising Standards – Improving Performance in the NHS was launched in May 2003 and gave details of a new NHS improvement programme, including £200m of financial support, to help all hospitals achieve NHS Foundation Trust status within four or five years.

Creation of Foundation Trusts
The Health Select Committee published its *Report into NHS Foundation Trusts* in May 2003. The *Government's Response to the Health Committee's Report* into *NHS Foundation Trusts* was published on 7 July 2003. The response explains the features of NHS Foundation Trusts in detail and clarifies several aspects of its policy.

The Health and Social Care (Community Health and Standards) Act came into force in November 2003. It provided legislation to decentralise control from Whitehall and established NHS Foundation Trusts.

On 20 January 2004, the Secretary of State confirmed his support for 24 NHS trusts in their bids to become the first wave of NHS Foundation Trusts.

These NHS Trusts applied to the Office of the Independent Regulator for authorisation to become NHS Foundation Trusts. (The final decision as to whether a trust can become an NHS Foundation Trust rests with the Independent Regulator).

The Government's aim is that by 2008, all NHS trusts would have reached a standard which would enable them to apply for NHS Foundation Trust status. This would ensure that throughout the country there are high performing organisations which are empowered to deliver high quality services to local people, so that no part of the NHS is left behind.

The first NHS Foundation Trusts were established in April 2004. There are now 31 NHS Foundation Trusts.*

NHS dentistry

General dental practitioners (gdps) are paid by the Dental Practice Board for each item of treatment they carry out. There are set fees for all types of treatment on adult patients. There are also capitation payments. These are fees for patients under the age of 18 who have been accepted into capitation for the care and treatment necessary to secure and maintain oral health. The dentist also receives a special fee for patients with severe mental or physical handicap.

Private dentists are paid directly by the patient and can set their own fees. Growth of private dentistry at the expense of the National Health Service is a manifestation of a more general trend towards consumerism across all healthcare services. Private payment for dental treatment has been increasing since the early 1990s when a cut in the NHS fee scales led to widespread dissatisfaction among dentists. Increasingly, general dental practitioners have reduced their reliance on the NHS as a source of clinical activity, choosing to treat adults privately in order to improve job satisfaction and give income appropriate to the work undertaken.

Many believe that NHS fees are at a level that threatens quality as well as restricting choice of dental treatment. Cosmetic dentistry and more advanced specialised treatments are areas that have become increasingly popular within the private sector, largely consumer led.

---

*Source: A Guide to Foundation Trusts; Department of Health, January 2004.

NHS Dentistry: Options for Change

The New Service

The *NHS Dentistry: Options for Change* report proposes a new NHS dental service for England. Fifty four years after the foundation of the NHS, this report contains recommendations for radical changes, designed to provide a first class NHS dental service, responsive to local needs.

Health policy on dental services has lagged decades behind other health sectors. Over the decade since 1992, dentists' commitment to the NHS has reduced, leading to access difficulties. The recommendations in *Options for Change* are designed to build on recent initiatives aimed at modernising NHS dentistry. They establish a new foundation for taking forward an NHS dental service for all. Dentists and dental professionals have been discontented for a long time with the framework for delivering care within the NHS.

These proposals will enable them to provide high quality NHS care, shaped for the needs of patients in the 21st century.

A new NHS dental service should be a universal system, but it should also meet the needs of particular groups in the population, with referral to specialist NHS dental services as necessary. Furthermore, the new service should allow the dental team, for the first time, to focus on preventive measures to combat dental disease, and to tackle the serious oral health inequalities, particularly in children, in the country.

Meeting Patients' Needs

NHS Dentistry: Options for Change proposes a new foundation for NHS dental services, working within NHS structures:- New standards of care, supported by a new payment system, and proposals for a modern workforce to meet the needs of today and tomorrow. The report proposes that its recommendations are first tested and evaluated carefully in demonstration sites by dentists and Primary Care Trusts in selected areas, using Personal Dental Services (PDS) contract flexibilities. This will allow change to be introduced and tested carefully and with the consent of all concerned. Over time, a new NHS dental service should be available to everyone.

Putting Patients' Interests First

In line with the *NHS Plan* and *Modernising NHS Dentistry*, the *NHS Dentistry: Options for Change* proposals put patients, and the patient experience, at the heart of the new NHS dental service. Currently, patients find care options confusing and dentists have the task of explaining to patients their choices.

There is an over-complex NHS regime, and then a mixture of private and NHS care available in many practices. The experience of grappling with the current systems often leaves patients feeling disempowered and dentists disengaged.

Under the new proposals, NHS treatment options to maintain dental health for children, for adults of working age, for older people, and for those with particular needs – would be evidence-based and regulated by service agreements with the dental profession. Patient-focused standards of care would be introduced into all NHS primary dental services.

NHS patient charges, currently numbering over 300 individual items, would be simplified. The responsibilities of each member of the dental team and their professional duties of care would be clarified. Where patients require further specialist care, referrals would be made to appropriate specialists.

NHS and Private Dental Care

In a new NHS dental service, the range of treatments provided by the NHS would be clear to patients. Some patients will want to choose treatments which are effective and valuable to them, but which fall outside NHS care because they do not follow agreed NHS clinical pathways. In a modern society, such choices should be available, and many or most general dental practitioners offer these treatments already. In the proposed new NHS primary care service, dentists may offer both NHS and private dental care. Dentists who provide these additional private services would give information and advice on private treatment choices and methods of payment. The choices for patients should be much more transparent than at present.

Developing the Dental Team

The proposed NHS dental service would be governed by a set of standards, drawn up between patients groups, the dental professionals, the NHS and Government and these would be available to all patients. The new dental service would involve all members of the dental team, which would allow new roles and responsibilities to emerge.

Over time, with investment in new premises and in team development, dentists would be encouraged to become clinical leaders, assessing need, co-ordinating the different skills of the team, and actively supporting the oral health wishes of their patients.

In this way there would be new opportunities for all parts of the dental team to meet the challenges of tomorrow.

Seven elements of a new NHS dental service*

- The service would be available to everyone who wants it, including people with special needs, however they contact the NHS.
- It would be based on a range of services to achieve dental health and, by preventing illness, to maintain dental health and address oral health inequalities.
- It would be governed by service agreements for children's health, adults' health, and older people's health as well as specialist services.
- NHS services and standards of care would be clear to all users.
- NHS charges and payments would be simplified.
- Referrals would be made to specialist NHS services as appropriate.

*Source: NHS Dentistry: Options for Change, August 2002.

- Private dental services, not available on the NHS, would be clearly identified in practice prospectuses and within treatment plans.

Dental laboratory services

The working environment in which dental technicians operate is subject to constant change:

a) Through research, development and professional clinical trials, some of the work undertaken and materials used are becoming more complex; this applies to all the main dental specialties.
b) The management of laboratory work must be able to cater for a number of different situations including routine, specialist and ad hoc requests as well as emergency treatment demands.
c) With the increasing complexity of dentistry, it will be important to ensure that technical services, and clinical dental education, continue to be maintained at an adequate level.
d) Particularly in orthodontics, the turn round time for some technical work requires to be short to protect compliance and clinical co-operation of patients.
e) The emphasis placed by patients upon dental health and appearance, together with scientific and technological innovation, has led to an increase in the workload of technicians and also requires them to be as up to date as possible on changing requirements, materials and techniques.

Today's changing business and working environment requires that dental laboratory managers possess a wide range of knowledge, skills and competencies, which include a good understanding of how management processes and functions are applied and how they can be used.

Previous research by the author[5] has shown that dental laboratories within the commercial sector provide a varied and extensive service to their customers in terms of both cost and the type of service offered.

Those laboratories with a large customer base within the United Kingdom and Europe provide an extensive service in all areas of dental technology. Some of these larger laboratories have contracts with Dental Hospitals and Schools, Community Health Centres and the Armed Forces.

The smaller laboratories tend to offer a more specialised service which enables them to keep the prices competitive with their larger counterparts. The majority of laboratories offer a two tier system of prices, one for the NHS and one for the private sector.

There is a difference between the commercial sector and dental hospitals over the qualification requirement for the employment of staff. The working practices and procedures of commercial laboratories also differ, in that:

* non qualified staff may be employed to undertake the routine work
* the more skilled tasks may be undertaken by qualified/non qualified staff known as skilled process workers
* technical staff may construct individual stages of work rather than the entire restoration

By using this method of production the laboratories are able to keep production costs low and productivity high. The policy of employing single skill technicians means that they are more proficient in their particular skill, although this does not automatically mean better restorations for the patient.

Factors that affect hospital laboratory services are the fluctuations in type and volume of work, difficulties of recruitment and retention of technical staff, and often the lack of information on the specific requirements for the undergraduate/postgraduate student teaching programmes.

Previous research[6] has shown that the majority of managers are concerned with the problem of developing managerial strategies appropriate to changing conditions. The word *change* has become part of everyday language. Managers are being required to look at ways of developing a flexible service which is *proactive* and capable of providing a varied and extensive service to patients in terms of the type and quality of work while maintaining an efficient and viable service.

Visits to hospital and commercial laboratories showed that there are some well managed successful laboratories, small and large. However there are some that could significantly improve the overall efficiency, standard and quality of service by careful strategic planning and development of management skills to the same degree as their technical ones.

Private sector companies

Case studies carried out on private sector companies by the author has shown that strategy is driven by a clear *vision* for the future and in some cases triggered by perceived opportunities. The strategy was developed by the Chief Executive and/or Management Board, or in smaller companies by the vision of the Managing Director.[6] Decisions were made in order to achieve the companies' objectives and responsibility to its stakeholders.

A variety of objectives could be discerned from the studies, ranging from localised structural and operational change to organisational and cultural change that involved the company, people, customers and suppliers.

Depending on the circumstances or constraints, strategy development took different forms. These could be deliberate and conscious decisions that were made to shape future strategy in order to expand the company's range and quality of products/service to its customers; strategy programmes resulting from the constraints and competitive environment faced by the company, and changes planned and based on the principles on which the company was founded.

The case studies showed that some companies' objectives and strategy were changed deliberately in response to environmental changes, because the company itself had changed as it had grown and gained experience, or through the need to develop and expand its products or service.

Also highlighted was the need for company strategies to be carefully planned through a thorough analysis of their present situation and future objectives. In circumstances where the future is uncertain, it is unwise to make detailed plans for the future and therefore a more flexible approach has to be adopted by setting short term targets, adapting to the environment and learning from experience while continuing in the desired direction to achieve success.

There was ample demonstration of the manner in which companies are changing not just their internal relationships but also their external ones. Also highlighted was the priority companies give their customers and the urgency with which they are considered.

The focus of the business strategy for all the companies in the study was customer satisfaction, which means identifying and satisfying customer needs, providing the benefits sought, and doing so better than their competitors while making satisfactory profit. In other words gaining differential advantage by giving better value.

Why change?

Organisations, whether they are private sector companies or non-profit public sector organisations, have to meet customer demands if they are to succeed. This was obvious from the case studies, but is now also true in the public sector for organisations such as schools, universities and NHS Trust hospitals.

As customer needs alter, so business must change by anticipating customer wants, leading these where appropriate as well as responding to them. The emphasis today is to focus on the customer so that all managers are concerned with leading their organisation, department, unit or team to enable planning for the future and work to be carried out successfully in response to the needs of the market and/or customer[6] .

Hospital and commercial dental laboratories, like the companies studied, have a number of functions to perform. They exist to achieve objectives and provide a high quality service and standard of products to clinical staff and students and general dental practitioners (gdps).

The objectives of any strategy and/or planned change undertaken by companies and laboratories cannot be achieved by the efforts of individuals on their own. It is through the co-operative action of all the people within the company or laboratory that success is achieved.

Dental laboratories are set up to serve a number of different purposes and meet a variety of needs required from their customers. The structure, management and working practices vary because of differences in the nature and type of laboratory.

The underlying theme of this book will be to look at the methods and their effectiveness in the planning and implementation of strategic change, and the role of management as an integrated activity.

The success of the change process is affected by a number of variables. Dental laboratories, like companies, need to be efficient in doing the 'right things first time every time' with the optimum use of available resources. Performance should be related to improved service delivery.

Laboratories must also ensure that they meet satisfactorily the demands and requirements of customers. A key factor in the effectiveness of a laboratory must be the successful management of change and innovation in response to the constant changes in its internal and external environment.

To be effective, change has to encompass, and treat as independent, at least seven variables: strategy, structure, people, management/leadership style, symptoms and procedures, guiding concepts and values (i.e. culture) and the strengths and skills within the laboratory.

The need for a clear and defined vision and strategy is essential. It provides a framework in which priorities can be set and decisions made. It provides direction to staff and gives them confidence that management knows why change is happening and how they can play a role in it. The rationale for introducing change in strategic terms should be linked to a review of the principal strengths, weaknesses, opportunities and threats in the existing operational procedures, skills, structure and service delivery to the customers.

Chapter 2

AN INTRODUCTION TO STRATEGY AND STRATEGIC MANAGEMENT

Introduction

Strategy is a complex topic. However, the underlying principles are essentially simple. There is *no best way* of managing strategic change and no single technique or model can provide either the right answer concerning what an organisation should do, or superior and crystal clear insight into a situation. Instead managers should utilise the range of theories and concepts which are available, adapting them to meet their own situation and circumstances.[7]

At the same time, a study of strategic change in a variety of different companies is valuable. An examination of outcomes, followed by an analysis of the decisions which led to these relative successes and failures, is rich in learning potential. Examples should not be confined to just one sector. Manufacturing and service businesses, the private sector and non profit organisations are all relevant.

Everyone who can make or influence decisions which impact upon the strategic effectiveness of a company should have at least a basic understanding of the concepts and processes of strategy. The processes will often be informal, and the outcomes not documented clearly. But they still exist, and managing the processes effectively determines the company's future. This also applies to dental laboratory managers.

Without this understanding, dental laboratory managers often fail to appreciate the impact of their decisions and actions for other people within the laboratory. They are less likely to be able to learn from observing and reflecting upon the actions of others.

They are also more likely to miss or misjudge new opportunities and growing threats in the laboratory's environment.

There is a certain consensus of opinion with regard to the basic features regarding strategic management and strategic decisions. Burnes[8] states that most writers agree with Johnson and Scholes[9] who describe strategy as:

- concerning the full scope of an organisation's activities
- concerning the process of matching the organisation's activities to its environment
- concerning the process of matching its activities to its resource capabilities
- having resource implications
- affecting operational decisions
- being affected by the values and beliefs of those who have power in an organisation
- affecting the long term direction of an organisation

Dental laboratories will succeed if their strategies are appropriate for the circumstances they face, feasible in respect of their resources, skills and capabilities, and desirable to their important stakeholders. Laboratories fail when their strategies fail to meet the expectations of these stakeholders or produce outcomes which are undesirable to them. To succeed long term, dental laboratories must find suitable ways for creating and adding value for their customers while remaining cost effective and viable. A culture of internal co-operation and customer orientation, together with a willingness to learn, adapt and change is ideal. Alliances and good working relationships with suppliers and customers are critically important as well.

Challenges

Many dental laboratories must compete in uncertain, dynamic and turbulent environments where pressures are continuous and changing.

New opportunities and threats appear at short notice and require a speedy response. Strategies which were appropriate yesterday are unlikely to be suitable today let alone tomorrow.

As a result there are a number of major challenges for dental laboratories. The challenges do not have black and white answers. Instead they represent paradoxes or dilemmas for laboratories, who have to make decisions about how they are going to deal with them.

There are five important challenges:

1. There is a need for dental laboratories to develop a culture of change orientation without losing internal cohesion and stability. This implies an explicit and shared vision of where the laboratory is heading.
2. There is a need to decentralise and give departmental managers more delegated authority whilst not losing sight (at laboratory management level) of the changes they are introducing.
3. There is then a trade-off between such empowerment (delegating responsibility in order to make the laboratory more effective) and the greater efficiencies often yielded by centralised control and systems which harness the latest information technology.
4. There is a need to act quickly in response to opportunities and threats, but not at the expense of product and service quality – achieving high quality at the same time as improving efficiencies.

    These four challenges are all related.
5. Finally there is the dilemma of the economic recession and lack of funding/cash flow which results in the laboratory cutting back and controlling its costs. This can have an effect on productivity, resources and staff.

Dental laboratory managers must react quickly and behave opportunistically in rapidly changing environments. Consequently they must also plan how their departmental managers/staff can first be put in a position to be willing and able to accept responsibility, use their initiative and take appropriate risks. These latter issues are an integral part of the laboratory's culture, and are highly dependent upon reward systems.

Definitions

Strategies are means to an end, and concern the purpose and objectives of the organisation. They are things that businesses do, the paths they follow, and the decisions they take, in order to reach certain points and levels of success.

Strategic management is a process which needs to be understood more than a discipline which can be taught. It is the process by which organisations determine their purpose, objectives and desired levels of attainment; decide upon actions for achieving these objectives in an appropriate timescale, and frequently in a changing environment; implement those actions; and assess progress and results.

Whenever and wherever necessary the actions may be changed or modified. The magnitude of these changes can be dramatic and revolutionary, or more gradual and evolutionary.[7]

The three essential elements are:

* *Awareness*: understanding the strategic situation
* *Formulation*: choosing suitable strategies
* *Implementation*: making the chosen strategies happen

On their own, good ideas are inadequate. They must be made to work and bring results.

The three elements are shown in Figure 1. Monitoring progress continuously is essential if the dental laboratory is to keep up to date with the strategic situation.

Levels of strategy

There are three linked and interdependent levels of strategy. *Competitive strategy* is concerned with creating and maintaining a competitive advantage in each and every area of the business. It

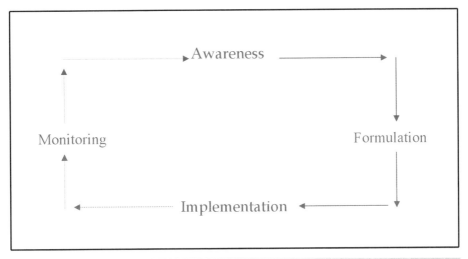

Figure 1: *Strategic management: awareness, formulation, implementation*

can be achieved through any one function or combination of several.[7]

For each functional area of the business, such as production, marketing and human resources, the company will have a *functional strategy*. It is important that these functional strategies are designed and managed in a co-ordinated way, such that they interrelate with each other and, at the same time, collectively allow the competitive strategies to be implemented properly.

Successful functional and competitive strategies add value which is important to the organisation's stakeholders, especially its customers, and which helps to distinguish the organisation from its competitors.

External networks which create *synergy* by linking a company closely with its suppliers, distributors and/or customers are also a source of added value, but these are examples of corporate strategy.

Corporate strategy, essentially and simply, is deciding what business the organisation should be in, and how the overall group of activities should be structured and managed. The term *strategic perspective* is often used to describe the range and diversity of activities; and then each should have a *distinctive competitive position*.

Managing change and the environment

Ideas for change and improvement can originate with people anywhere in the dental laboratory, not just the laboratory manager. They are the people who are closest to the customers, suppliers, and production areas, and who first realise when competitors are making changes or when changes are required within the laboratory. Their contributions must be harnessed in some way, and they must be encouraged and empowered to make any changes which can strengthen competitiveness and improve the efficiency and effectiveness of the laboratory. If they are to do this, they have to be rewarded for using initiative and taking risks, but the whole process must be monitored and controlled.

Some changes, particularly major ones, certainly will start with dental laboratory managers, and they will seek to persuade others to support their ideas. They will be looking to *manage change*. Others will emerge from the ongoing *decision processes*, and these depend upon how good people are at learning, sharing ideas and working as a team. People can learn from colleagues in their own laboratory, from competitors and from other different companies and laboratories if they are alert and aware of events.

Changes to a dental laboratory's strategy will frequently involve some detailed analysis and planning, although on some occasions some managers will act more intuitively. However, changes with functional strategies can often be made on a trial and error basis. Ideas for improvements can be tried out experimentally, and developed seriously if the trials seem favourable.

The success of any dental laboratory manager in responding to change pressures, and managing the process of change is very dependent upon the values and commitment of its employees – the culture of the laboratory. Effective strategic management also depends upon the abilities and style of the *strategic leader* (laboratory manager), who is responsible for changes in the laboratory strategy.

Strategic management is dynamic; strategies need to be

reviewed and revised all the time. Figure 2 provides an interpretation of the important elements in strategic management.

Strategic management involves **awareness** of how successful and strong a dental laboratory and its strategies are, and of how circumstances are changing.

At any time, previously sound products, services and strategies are likely to be in decline, or threatened by competition. As this happens new windows of opportunity will be opening for the vigilant and proactive competitors.[7]

New **strategies must be created**. Sometimes this will be part of a formal planning process; at other times the changes will emerge as managers try out new ideas. The process involved in designing and carrying through the changes must be managed, monitored and controlled.

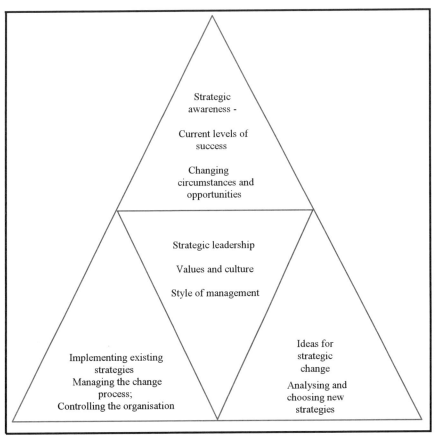

Figure 2: *Strategic management*

Proper **implementation** is critically important. The relative success of the laboratory manager in dealing with these strategic issues will be dependent upon the culture and values, and the strength and style of the manager as the **strategic leader**. Consequently these are shown at the very heart of the triangle, impacting on, and ideally blending together, the other issues.

Simply, it is the *heart* which determines the ability of the laboratory manager to learn from his own success and failures, from external stakeholders, and from changes in the environmental forces, and, as a result of this, learning to act positively at the appropriate time.

Chapter 2 – Key Points

- Strategies are means to ends. The ends concern the purpose and objectives of the dental laboratory. Laboratory managers must have a strategy for the whole of the dental laboratory which reflects the range and diversity of activities and a competitive strategy for each activity.
- Strategic management is the process by which laboratory managers formulate, implement, monitor and control their strategies.
- There are three levels of strategy:
  Corporate – the scope of the business as a whole
  Competitive – for each business area
  Functional – which provide the competitiveness
- Effective strategic management implies that laboratories manage their resources in such a way that they both respond to, and manage, their environment.
- The culture and style of management are critical factors, and the impact of the strategic leader should not be underestimated.
- Strategic management involves awareness of how successful the laboratory is and how circumstances are changing.
- Strategies are created through a formal planning process.
- The business environment can be evaluated by the expectations of the stakeholders.
- To succeed laboratories must find suitable ways of creating and adding value for their customers.
- All employees can make or influence decisions. Ideas for change can originate from people anywhere in the laboratory.
- **The model used in Figure 2 summarises the key points in this Chapter**.

Chapter 3

EFFECTIVE STRATEGIC MANAGEMENT

Introduction

Thompson[10] refers to David Marshall, who had experience in marketing and corporate planning with Special Components, a small subsidiary of Universal Engineering, and who used charts to highlight the central themes of strategic management when working on a project for the parent company. His diagrams concentrated on the **concept** of strategy rather than providing a detailed explanation of a company's strategic planning system. He felt that it was essential to begin with a description of how the company sought to be an effective competitor and continue to provide value for their customers.

David Marshall used the EVR Congruence framework (Environment, Values, Resources) together with other concepts and frameworks, to illustrate how Special Components sought to match its resources with the needs and expectations of its customers. He realised that it would also be helpful if he explained the mission statement for the organisation. He knew that a good mission statement provides a useful summary of the purpose and direction of the business and thereby helps determine appropriate objectives and strategies.[10]

Environment – Values – Resources

Strategies are being managed effectively when the dental laboratory's/company's resources are deployed efficiently, and respond and adapt to changes in the environment. Simply, it has strengths which allow it to capitalise on opportunities and deal with potential threats.

A basic understanding of this comes from an analysis of the laboratory's <u>s</u>trengths, <u>w</u>eaknesses, <u>o</u>pportunities and <u>t</u>hreats – a **SWOT** analysis. Sometimes this is used to help clarify the current situation; it is arguably more valuable when used as a basis for projecting forward. Future opportunities, where the laboratory's strengths can be utilised to advantage should be sought; at the same time future threats which might critically expose the weaknesses of the business must be identified and dealt with.[10]

EVR (Environment, Values, Resources) Congruence, Figure 3, is a refined version of this idea.

- **Environment**: What do customers and other stakeholders demand? Which competitor strengths have to be bettered?
- **Resources**: Which functions are (or will be) critically important? Why, and how, must they be deployed to satisfy changing market needs?
- **Values**: What will it feel like to work in the dental laboratory? Which values and behaviours will be required for (i) adding value and (ii) adapting and changing?

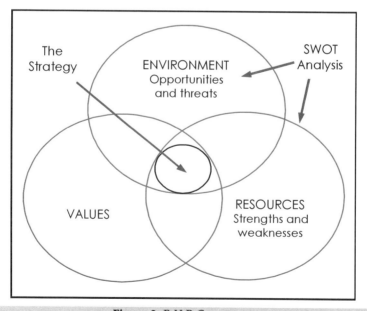

Figure 3: *E-V-R Congruence*

Dental laboratory managers must look for new ideas which will bring new growth and prosperity, improve overall efficiency or help achieve other objectives which are regarded as important. Awareness, formulation and implementation were introduced as three key aspects of strategic management in Chapter 2.

EVR can be used to focus on two basic questions:

1. What will our major stakeholders expect from us in the future, and how are we going to satisfy their changing needs?
2. What are our most valuable skills and capabilities, and what new opportunities are there for exploiting these abilities?

This type of analysis, however it may be carried out, should allow the manager to make decisions concerning future targets and the actions which will be required to achieve them.[10] These points are illustrated in Figure 4.

It is useful if this thinking and analysis can take place within a clear framework of a corporate direction and purpose, the *mission* of the dental laboratory.

The *mission statement* is useful for providing direction and guidance. Ideally the mission will state the basic purpose of the business, together with a summary of appropriate activities, how

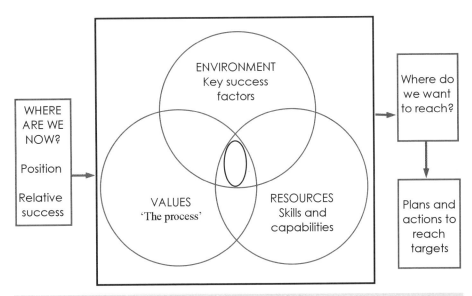

Figure 4: *Strategic thinking*

progress towards achievement of the purpose might be managed and monitored and how the company might create competitive advantage.

It should be relevant for all the stakeholders, and also be understood and supported by all the company's employees.[7]

In summary the mission should:

- define the targeted business activities
- encapsulate long term objectives
- highlight how the company is differentiated from its competitors
- be relevant for all the stakeholders, including employees, and gain their commitment and support.[10]

Many companies, however, publish mission statements which are wordy and which do not meet the criteria for an effective statement as previously stated. In addition, or possibly as an alternative, some organisations adopt vision statements, which typically express the company's *vision* of some future state.

Strategy statements

The mission provides a valuable starting point for establishing more specific objectives and strategies, and in turn the performance of the organisation should be assessed against both the mission and the objectives, Figure 5.[10]

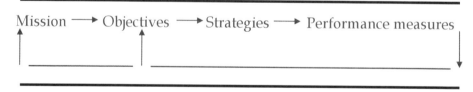

Mission ⟶ Objectives ⟶ Strategies ⟶ Performance measures

Figure 5: *Mission statements*

Typical objectives will include sales volume and revenue, production costs, customer complaints and delivery times. It is also useful to have targets, albeit less specific, for new product developments and other financial targets.

When timescales are applied, these specific objectives constitute milestones and their achievement should be measured and recorded.

Assuming that the objectives help the organisation towards the achievement of its purpose, progress in this direction can also be measured.

Figure 6 draws upon the above points and provides an outline framework for a strategy statement. Ideally the managers in an organisation will be in a position to complete a chart such as this, and agree upon the issues and their implications.[7]

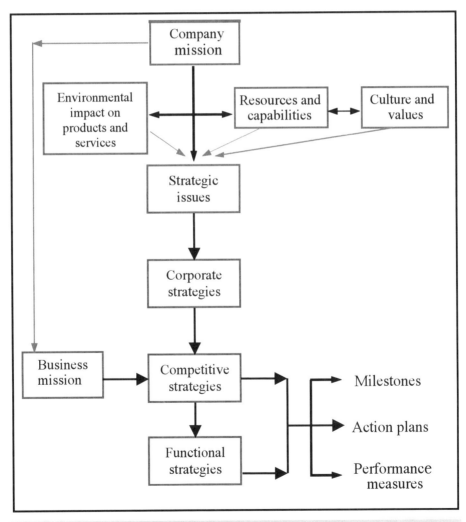

Figure 6: *An outline strategy statement*

The figure begins at the top with the company *mission statement*. In the context of this the companies should evaluate E, V, and R in order to tease out any important and current *strategic issues* which need attention.[7]

In the light of current and projected issues, *corporate, competitive* and *functional strategies* can be reviewed in order to establish short term *objectives, action plans* and *performance targets*. Figure 6 provides both a broad outline framework for thinking and planning and a set of headings for summarising and explaining current strategies.

It would be valuable if all the managers of dental laboratories could express the current strategic situation in this way. This type of analysis will help to determine whether current strategies are the right ones, and highlight where businesses might look to make changes.

Chapter 3 – Key Points

- An analysis of strengths, weaknesses, opportunities and threats (SWOT analysis) is a useful framework for strategic awareness.
- Dental laboratories need to match their resources with their environment.
- Because the environment can be unpredictable, changing this matching process needs to be managed. Values and culture determine the organisation's ability to create and maintain an effective match. A more useful framework which encapsulates this theme is E-V-R Congruence (Figure 3).
- The environment and the laboratory's stakeholders determine the key success factors, those factors that a laboratory really needs to address for long term competitive advantage and strategic success.
- A clear and understood mission statement, which explains the basic purpose of the business, is helpful both for strategy planning and explaining current strategies.

Chapter 4

ENSURING STRATEGIC SUCCESS

Adding value

A business must add value if it is to be successful. As supply potential has grown to exceed global demand in the majority of industries, adding value has become increasingly important. In simple terms the extent of the value added is the difference between the value of the outputs from a business and the cost of the inputs or resources.[10]

It is therefore important to use all the resources efficiently and properly. It is also critical to ensure that the potential value of the outputs is maximised by ensuring they fully meet the needs of the customers for whom they are intended. A business achieves this when it sees its customers' objectives as its own objectives and enables its customers to easily add more value or, in the case of end consumers, feel they are gaining true value for money.

The important elements are:

- understanding and being close to customers
- a commitment to quality
- a high level of all round service
- speedy reaction to competitive opportunities and threats
- innovation

Competencies and capabilities

Core competencies and capabilities concern the way that resources are managed for strategic effectiveness.

Core competencies are distinctive skills, normally relating to particular products, services or technologies which help a business to differentiate its products or services and thereby create a competitive advantage. The more distinctive and hard to copy the skills are, the greater the advantage. Simply having the skills is not enough. They have to be carefully managed and exploited, and they need improving all the time as competitors are always going to match them.

Strategic capabilities are conceptually similar but they are the real process skills as distinct from the core technologies and products. They can be used to create competitive advantage because they add value for money.

The ability to develop or introduce new products quickly is an example. Skills and practices developed in one area of business can be transferred to others if there is an attempt to learn and share. Information management harnessing the potential of new technologies is an increasingly critical skill.

Competitive advantage

Competitive advantage implies a distinct and, ideally, sustainable edge over competitors.

Thompson[10] refers to Porter[11] who has shown how companies can seek a broad advantage within industry or focus on one or a number of distinct segments. Porter argues that advantage can accrue from:

1. *Cost leadership*, whereby a company's prices are around the average of the market (with a product or service) but it enjoys superior profits because its costs are lower than those of its rivals.
2. *Differentiation*, where value is added in areas of real signifi-cance for its customers who are willing to pay a premium price for the distinctiveness. A range of differential products or services, each designed to appeal to a different segment, is possible, as it focuses on just one segment.

Speed (i.e. quicker new product development/introduction) and a fast reaction to both opportunities and threats can provide advantage, essentially by reducing costs and differentiating products and services.

The concept of a value chain, developed by Porter, categorises the organisation as a series of processes generating value for customers and other stakeholders. By examining each value-creating activity, it is possible to identify sources of potential cost leadership and differentiation.

The value chain (Figure 7) splits activities into: (i) primary activities – in-bound logistics, operations, outward logistics, marketing/ sales and service, and (ii) secondary activities – infrastructure, human resource management, technology development and procurement. These secondary activities take place in order to support the primary activities. For example, the firm's infrastructure (e.g. management, finance and buildings) serves to support the five primary functions. While each activity generates 'value', the linkages between the activities are critical. Consider the interface between in-bound logistics and operations. A just-in-time logistics system, supported by computerised stock ordering

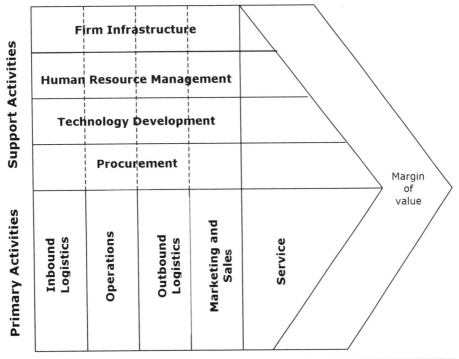

Figure 7: *Michael Porter's Value Chain*

(technology development – secondary activity) could reduce stock costs and enhance the quality of products manufactured in the operations phase of the chain, thus enhancing the overall value generated by the process. The value generated is shown as the **'margin of value'** in Figure 7.

The value chain provides an additional framework to analyse competitive advantage. It helps identify the key skills, processes and linkages required to generate success.

Real competitive advantage implies that companies are able to satisfy customer needs and deliver value more efficiently than their competitors. It does not come simply from being different. It is achieved if and when *real value* is added for the customers. This often requires companies to stretch their resources to achieve higher returns. Improved productivity may be involved; ideally employees will come up with *innovations*, new and better ways of doing things for customers. These innovations can result in lower costs, differentiation, or faster response to opportunities and threats, the basis of competitive advantage.

Such innovations also requires that employees are *empowered*. Authority, responsibility and accountability will decentralise allowing employees to make decisions for themselves, and be willing and able to look for improvements. Basically managers should seek to encourage ordinary people to achieve extraordinary results. This will only happen if achievement is properly recognised, and initiative and success rewarded.

Competitive advantage is also facilitated by good internal and external communications – achieving one of the potential benefits of linkages. Without this, businesses cannot share and learn best practice. Moreover information is a fundamental aspect of organisational control. Companies can learn from suppliers, distributors, customers and from other members within the organisation, and from its competitors.

Businesses should never overlook opportunities for communicating their achievements, strengths and successes. Image and reputations are vitally important as they help to retain business.

Figure 8 summarises, diagramatically, the points that have been discussed.[10]

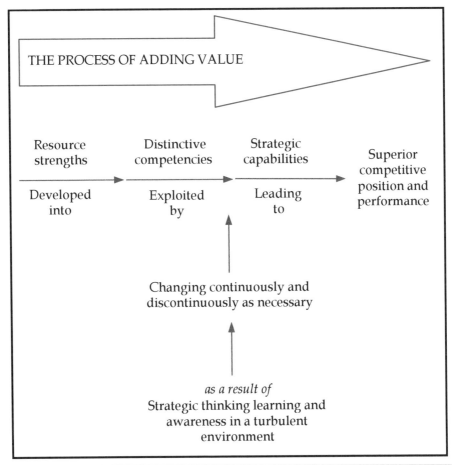

Figure 8: *Adding value for sustained competitive advantage*

Strategic regeneration

Strategic regeneration refers to simultaneous changes to strategies and structures in the search for:

- long term product or service leadership, which is dictated by the *environment*
- long term cost leadership, which is *resource* dependent
- product and service excellence, doing things faster than competitors without sacrificing quality; that is, paying attention to essential *values*

Strategies have to be reinvented, new products and services

should be created while at the same time looking for ways of adding extra value.

In thinking ahead, businesses should consider both products or services and core competencies; concentrating on products encourages a search for new competitive opportunities.[7]

Structural changes are designed to improve resource efficiency and effectiveness. The current trends are:

- *down-sizing* – splitting the business into small, autonomous decentralised units.
- *delayering* – using the power and potential of information technology for reducing the number of layers of management, in order to speed up decision making.
- *process re-design* – reviewing and re-designing processes in order that tasks can be performed better and more quickly.

Empowerment and teamworking are also seen as essential for creating the values necessary to enable these types of change to take place.

Strategic regeneration can be justified as essential, exciting and rewarding but there are likely to be major barriers when applying these ideas. The most obvious problems are:

- the quality of leadership which is required to provide the necessary drive and direction.
- an ability to create an internal culture of change. The most powerful inhibitors will be the experienced, established managers whose ideas and methods have become out of date.
- an uncertainty about changing needs and competitor activities.

Thompson[10] refers to Pascal[12] who uses the word *transforma-tional* to describe organisations which succeed with simultaneous strategic and cultural change. He also refers to Senge[13] who states that these become *learning organisations* which encourage contin-uous learning and knowledge generation at all levels, and have processes which can move knowledge around the organisation easily to where it can translate that knowledge quickly into changes in the way the organisation acts, both internally and externally.

Monitoring and evaluating performance

Good performance needs to be recognised quickly so it can be built on. Poor performance must also be identified so that it can be dealt with sooner rather than later. Ideally, a business should continuously measure customer perceptions of the level of service they are receiving, highlighting both the need and opportunities for improvement. Speedy action can then follow. Accurately measuring customer perceptions of services, however, is likely to prove more difficult than monitoring, say, sales and profit figures. The data must be collected externally and will be subjective. Nevertheless, in many instances, it is perfectly feasible to stay aware informally and be ready to react.[7]

Another difficulty with evaluating success is the fact that we may not be able to wholly explain why something is successful. If businesses are to build and remedy failure, they must be able to understand the causes. The outcomes of significant dental laboratory problems are obvious – loss of revenue, market share and profits; high labour turnover and absenteeism; increasing customer complaints. Managers may disagree on the causes and laboratories in difficulty may not have sufficient time for thorough analysis.

Dental laboratory managers may also assume that the success of the laboratory is the result of actions they have taken. Self-congratulation can lead to complacency and a lack of hunger for improvement, opening up opportunities for competitors. However, the success may not have been created directly by the managers; it may have resulted from competitor weaknesses or mistakes. Growth and continuing success, therefore, require both an understanding of the underlying causes and a commitment to improve and change. Strategies and ideas have to be applied to the particular situation. Success without change and improvement is also likely to be transient. There is no ideal long term strategic approach.

There are four important measures of performance, although we normally only attach significance to any two of these:[7]

1. *Efficacy* – the chosen strategy is capable of fulfilling the purpose for which it is intended.

2. *Economy* – doing things cost effectively. Resources should be managed at the lowest possible cost consistent with achieving quantity and quality targets.
3. *Efficiency* – doing things the best way. Resources should be deployed and utilised to maximise the returns from them.

For measuring economies and efficiencies, quantifiable objectives and targets must be set and agreed with managers. Progress can be measured and relative success evaluated.

4. *Effectiveness* – doing the correct things. Resources should be allocated to those activities which satisfy needs, expectations and priorities of the various stakeholders in the business.

Effectiveness invariably involves subjectivity as the measures involve perceptions of the outcomes and the variables being measured are mostly external rather than internal to the laboratory. For these reasons, it is generally more difficult to measure effectiveness, and consequently some managers will need to rely on indicators rather than formal measures.

Figure 9 explains how an efficient and effective business will create and sustain a positive performance cycle.

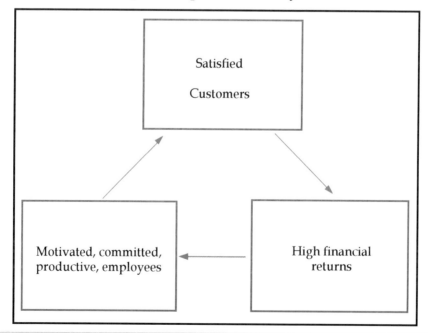

Figure 9: *The efficient-effective business*

Businesses must satisfy their customers, ideally out-performing their rivals to achieve this. As a consequence, loyal customers will pay premium prices for the values that have been added, yielding high financial returns. If these are used to reward managers and employees, then morale and commitment will improve. In turn this will motivate people, but it is essential to ensure that they do this productively and efficiently.[10]

Chapter 4 – Key Points

- Strategic success implies that stakeholder needs and expectations are being satisfied, and that a laboratory is out performing its competitors.
- Strategic success requires that value is added for customers through the supply chain. This implies internal and external linkages and co-operation. Businesses which are most successful in meeting key success factors are those which harness their core competencies and strategic capabilities to add value for customers.
- Strategy success is very dependent upon the internal linkages between businesses and functions, and the external alliances between members of the added value (or supply) chain. Interdependencies must be fostered if potential synergies (the added value from linkages) are to be attained.
- The basic themes for competitive advantage are lower costs, differentiation and speed. These again must represent added value for customers.
- Innovation, empowerment and the ability to learn and share are critical for achieving and maintaining competitiveness.
- The real challenge for many businesses' strategic regeneration is simultaneously changing strategies, structures and styles of managing the organisation.
- Feedback of progress is essential if businesses are to build on success and remedy weaknesses. Vigilance is important, and it is necessary to determine the most appropriate factors to measure.

Measuring effectiveness is more subjective, and quite possibly indicators, as opposed to definitive measures, may have to be used.

Chapter 5

MANAGEMENT AND STRATEGIC LEADERSHIP

This chapter is designed to help dental laboratory managers examine and compare the differences and processes of *Management* and *Leadership*.

Are we managers or leaders?

Most managers would probably claim to be able to exercise leadership in some form or another. A manager can be regarded as someone who by definition is assigned a position of leadership in an organisation, and it may therefore be reasonable to treat the terms leader and manager as meaning the same thing. But many people considered to be leaders are not actually managers. Many managers have duties and responsibilities that are not recognised as leadership. If we can first decide what leadership is, we can then ask which individuals possess or exercise it and which do not.[14]

Researchers have assumed that leaders and managers share the same characteristics and succeed or fail for the same reasons. Georgiadies and Macdonell[15] refer to Zaleznik[16] and, later, Burns[17], who contended that managers and leaders are different. Because they are different and because they play different roles, the authors argue that organisations must recognise the difference and plan their management development programme accordingly.

Abraham Zaleznik[16] added something very special to the leadership debate. In the article published in the *Harvard Business Review* entitled "Managers and leaders: are they different?". He states that we need to recognise that there really is a difference between being a manager and being a leader. He was the first one to communicate this difference, even if it is a concept that seems obvious to us now. His contentious article suggested that, not only are leaders and the different managers different kinds of people, but they do different things.

The difference between management and leadership

Managers have to be leaders, and leaders are often, but not always, managers. But a distinction can be made between the processes of management and leadership.

> *Management* is concerned with achieving results by effectively obtaining, deploying, utilising and controlling all the resources required, namely people, money, facilities, plant and equipment, information and knowledge.
> *Leadership* focuses on the most important resource – people. It is the process of developing and communicating a vision for the future, motivating people and gaining their commitment and engagement.

The distinction is important. Management is mainly about the provision, deployment and utilisation and control of resources. But where people are involved – and they almost always are – it is impossible to deliver results without providing effective leadership. It is not enough to be a good manager of resources – you also have to be a good leader of people.

> The key words describing leadership are: *change, vision, communication, proactive, high risk, and aligning and motivation.*
> The key words describing management are: *organising, planning and budgeting, rationality and control, reactive and risk averse.*

The differences in the roles are significant and there is scope for potential tension and conflict between them. Leaders are not necessarily managers but if they are in charge of resources, especially people, they have to act like managers to the extent that the use of those resources has to be organised, planned and controlled. But overemphasis on these managerial aspects of the role may prejudice leadership imperatives, especially the visionary, proactive and motivational aspects of leadership and the requirement to initiate and deliver change in an intuitive and emphatic way. Leaders tend to identify with the broader picture.

Managers as leaders

Hannagan[18] suggests that management implies leadership, and in fact the success or failure of managers can be judged on their leadership qualities. If the manager's role is to achieve organisational goals, then these are reached by showing people the way forward to find solutions and overcome obstacles.

In a constantly changing social, economic and technological environment, leadership has become a more important attribute of management than in the past. In a more static environment, controlling and organising might be seen as more important than leadership for most managers, but this has changed. It is not just senior managers who need to look forward in order to foresee the changes which are coming and to act accordingly.

Team managers and supervisors also have to implement change at their own level, to understand it and to take their working colleagues and subordinates along with them.

What is management?

Management has often been described as *"getting things done through people"*. This makes the important point that it is a purposeful activity. Management is concerned with defining ends as well as achieving them, deciding what to do and getting it done through individuals who are the most important resource available to managers. It is through this resource that other resources are managed. However, managers are ultimately accountable for the management of all other resources, including their own.[19]

Effective management

Effective management means managers ensuring that their organisational function or department operates effectively. They are accountable for attaining the required results, having been given authority over those working in the function or department.

Managers contribute to organisational success by getting the best out of other people but also by getting the best out of themselves.

Specifically, effective managers will:

- complete tasks that they expect to get done
- exercise visionary leadership
- plan the effective use of the resources allocated to them
- set the direction and ensure that everyone knows what is expected of them
- initiate and manage change designed to improve performance
- adapt and respond rapidly to changing demands and circumstances
- anticipate problems but deal promptly with those that arise unexpectedly
- monitor performance so that swift corrective action can be taken when necessary

Managers make an added value contribution when they make the best use of their resources to produce better results. They are concerned with productivity, which is the relationship between the input of resources and the output of goods or services. They plan ahead, maintain momentum and make things happen. They have to deal with immediate issues, responding to demands, but they are also proactive in developing new ways of doing things which anticipate problems.

Managers deal with programmes, processes, events and eventualities. They do this through people by the exercise of leadership, but in managing programmes, processes and events, managers have to be personally involved. They manage themselves as well as other people.

They cannot delegate everything and they frequently have to rely on their own resources to get things done. These resources include skill, know-how, competence, time, and their own reserves of resilience and determination.

All of these have to be deployed, not only in directing and motivating people but also in understanding situations and issues, problem analysis and definition, decision making, and taking action themselves as well as through others. They get support, advice and assistance from their own staff and specialists, but in the last analysis they are on their own. They have to make the decisions and they have to initiate and sometimes take the action.

Effective strategic leadership

The term strategic leader is used to describe the managers who head the organisation and who are primarily responsible for creating and implementing strategic change. Whilst the strategic leader has overall responsibility for managing strategy in the organisation it should not be thought that he or she is the sole source of thoughts and ideas. All employees can make a contribution and should be encouraged to do so. The more that people are invited to participate in debate and discussions concerning products, services, customers and the future, the more likely they are to accept the change.

The strategic leader, however, is in a unique position to gather and receive information about all aspects of the business, and it is incumbent on him or her to monitor the environment and the organisation and watch for opportunities and threats. The strategic leader will need both analytical skills and insight (or awareness) to provide an intuitive grasp of the situation that faces the organisation.

The way the organisation manages to grasp opportunities and overcome potential threats will be very dependent on the personal qualities and values of the strategic leader. Skills that are required of leaders therefore include:

- anticipatory skills in order to provide the foresight into a constantly changing situation.
- vision skills in order to lead the organisation towards the agreed goals and implement the strategic plans.
- value skills in order to be in touch with employees needs so that shared values and goals can be encouraged.
- empowerment skills, so that power is shared and employees are encouraged to share ideas.
- self-understanding in order that the strategic leader understands his or her own needs and those of the employees.

An effective strategic leader ensures that the organisation has a strategic vision which allows successful implementation.[9] The important direct or personal contributions concern vision and action, but the leader must also ensure that other key aspects are in place. These are: strategic vision, pragmatism, structure, communication, culture, change management and empowerment (Figure 10).[10]

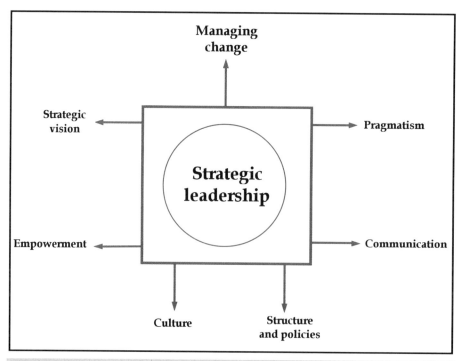

Figure 10: *Strategic leadership*

Strategic vision

A vision is the way we may link everyday events to a large set of values. Managers with vision are able to step back from a problem and see it in a much larger context.[15] At the heart of this is a clear, well understood and supported **mission** for the company. Employees must appreciate the fundamental purpose and be committed to its achievement. The mission will provide guidance and direction when managers make decisions and implement strategies determined by others.[10]

A mission statement is a complementary statement, much less visionary but nevertheless still of value in shaping the organisation's future. Although a vision is not a mission this is not to understate the importance of forming and using mission statements. The vision must stand on its own as a source of inspiration and direction. A vision establishes a clear sense of purpose, direction and desired future.

The mission may be the vision of the strategic leader; equally it may have been established by a predecessor. It is simply the responsibility of the strategic leader to ensure the strategies are in place, communicated and understood, together with the processes for managing the strategic change. Some leaders will be strategic visionaries who are also active in operations, others will contribute ideas and leadership but are happy to devolve responsibility.

As well as strategic vision it is necessary for the leader to build a structure and culture which captures the abilities and contributions of other managers and employees. The strategic leader's vision and his or her record of achievement are critical for obtaining and maintaining the confidence and support of the stakeholders.

The management of trust

Trust is hard to describe. People require repeated interaction with each other before they recognise it may exist. Leaders must continually strive to earn trust and maintain it. By clearly stating a vision and adhering to it, earns the company trust.

"Trust is an emotional glue that binds followers and leaders together. The accumulation of trust is a measure of the legitimacy of leadership. It cannot be mandated or purchased. It must be earned. Trust is the basic ingredient of all companies, the basic lubricant that maintains communities. It is as mysterious and illusive a concept as leadership and it is as important."[15]

In companies, trust between leaders and employees cannot exist without two conditions:

1. The leader's vision for the company must be clear, attractive and attainable. We tend to trust leaders who create these visions, since vision represents the context of shared beliefs in a common company purpose.
2. The leader's position must be clear. We tend to trust leaders when we know where they stand in relation to the company and how they position the company relative to the environment.

Positioning and trust are fundamental to all leadership activities:

- All leaders face the challenge of overcoming resistance to change. Some try to do this by simple exercise and control, but effective leaders learn that there are better ways to overcome resistance to change. This involves the achievement of voluntary commitment to shared values.
- A leader must reconcile the needs of different groups inside and outside the company. He or she must be sensitive to their various needs and have a clear sense of the company position.
- The leader is responsible for the set of ethics or norms that govern the behaviour of employees within the company. Leaders can establish a set of ethics by demonstrating their commitment to the set of ethics they are trying to institutionalise.

Trust, integrity and positioning are all different faces of a common requirement of leadership.

Chapter 5 – Key Points

- It can be argued that management is largely concerned with leadership because managers need to establish a sense of direction and to motivate people to move in that direction.
- Managers ensure that their organizational functions or departments operate effectively and are accountable for attaining results.
- Managers contribute to organizational success by getting the best out of other people and themselves.
- Added value is created by managers and the people they manage.
- The understanding of theories of leadership provides a basis for analysing leadership and management styles. This understanding is also a factor in the process of making decisions.
- The key aspects of effective leadership are vision and the ability to make things happen and bring results. It is necessary for the leader to ensure the company has a clear direction and purpose and is action orientated. Strategic decisions must be capable of implementation. The company must be able to respond to competitive and change pressures in the appropriate timescale.
- The strategic leader takes responsibility for ensuring that the needs and expectations of important stakeholders are being met.
- Visionary leaders have a vision for the future of the company and the commitment to making it happen. They understand intuitively which strategies will satisfy important stakeholders. They also rely heavily on other people, and consequently their skills at motivating, developing trust and inspiring others are critical issues.
- It is important that the style of leadership fits the strategic circumstances. Leaders must be flexible and capable of adapting.
- Leaders must continually strive to earn trust and maintain it.

Chapter 6

ORGANISATIONAL CULTURE

Introduction

Culture is significant and applies to all organisations including dental laboratories because it conveys a sense of identity and unity of purpose to staff. The success of an organisation in responding to change pressures and managing the process of change is highly dependent on the values and commitment of its staff. Culture is vitally important and not easily changed.

Thompson[7] states that in looking behind the visionary planning and adaptive incremental methods of strategy creation, examining why they are selected and preferred by different organisations, it is important to understand how the feelings and actions of people inside organisations affect strategy. People create change, and they are affected by changes happening elsewhere in the organisation.

Any group of people who live and work together for any length of time form and share certain beliefs about what is right and proper. They establish patterns of behaviour based on their beliefs, and their actions often become matters of habit which they follow unconsciously and routinely. These beliefs and ways of behaving constitute the organisation's culture.

The formation of, and any changes to, the culture of an organisation/laboratory is dependent upon leadership and the example of particular individuals, and their ability to control or influence situations. This in itself is dependent on a person's ability to obtain and use power.

Culture and power in an organisation often affect choice, incidence and application of the methods of strategy creation. The preferred method will reflect the values and preferences of the dental laboratory manager/strategic leader and the laboratory as a whole. It must though, be appropriate to the laboratory's strategic needs.

Culture and values determine the ability of an organisation to create and sustain a match between their resources and environment (E-V-R congruence). As industries and markets have become increasingly competitive, many organisations have come under pressure to change their cultures in order to be effective competitors and sustain E-V-R congruence.[7] In addition, the culture, political activity and the use of power and influence inside the organisation affect the outcomes from the decision making process which underpin the adaptive/incremental method.

People are concerned with the way an organisation reacts to potential opportunities or threats; affected organisations will not behave in the same way. Powerful external stakeholders can sometimes dictate the strategy of an organisation. Culture and power are such strong forces that any intended changes must take account of them. If they are overlooked, implementation may not happen. Culture is at the heart of all strategy creation and implementation in all dental laboratories.

Resources must be deployed and committed, but successful change also requires the 'right attitude' approach and commitment from people. Thompson[7] refers to this as 'mind set', which might, for example, reflect a strong customer and service focus, and further empowerment and consequent cultural change.

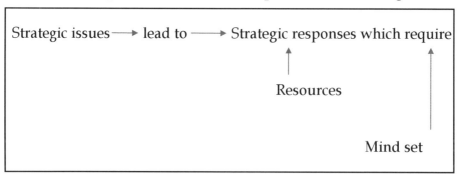

Strong cultures are an important strategic asset. An effective strategic leader will understand the culture in order that a vision can be pursued and intended strategies implemented.

Factors that influence culture

Factors that influence culture can be grouped into three areas as illustrated in Figure 11.[7]

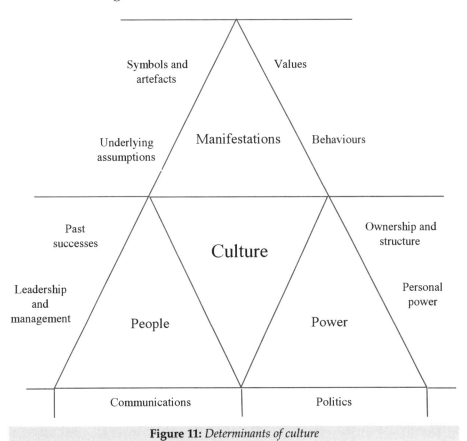

Figure 11: *Determinants of culture*

1. Manifestations

These include *symbols* and *artefacts* such as expensive offices, and the equipment, the products themselves, advertising, brand names and dress codes followed by employees. Some organisations will encourage smart casual wear rather than formal or corporate dress to foster an informal working environment. *Values* constitute ideas and convictions about what ought to be, which, with experience and learning, become beliefs and established practices. Examples of *behaviours* are speedy new product development, long working hours, formal management meetings and regular informal meetings or contacts with colleagues.

2. People

The category of people will include stories of *past successes* and the *present* strategic leadership and styles of management, which includes *innovation*. Linked to this is *communication*, an essential part of culture.

The organisation might be seen as open or closed, formal or informal. Ideally, employees from different parts of the organisation and different levels of hierarchy will feel willing and able to talk openly with each other, sharing problems, ideas and learning. Employees should also be trusted and empowered to the appropriate degree.

3. Power

Power is reflected in the *ownership* of the organisation or business. It may be a family company with strong concentrated power. A small group of institutional shareholders could control the business, in which case it is conceivable that short term financial targets will dictate strategies. Structural issues include the extent to which the organisation is centralised or decentralised, the role and contribution of corporate headquarters and control and reward systems.

The culture will influence the ability of a strategic visionary to sell his or her ideas to other members of the organisation and gain their support and commitment to change. Where environmental opportunities and threats arise continuously in a situation of competitive chaos, an organisation must be able to deal with them if it is to survive. It is the culture, with its combination of attitudes, values, perceptions and experiences which determines the outcomes and relative success. The structure must facilitate awareness, sharing and learning, and people must be willing and able to act.

People learn by doing and they must be able to learn from mistakes.

The reward system is critical here. Managers and employees should be praised and rewarded for exercising initiative and taking risks which prove successful; failures should not be sanctioned too harshly as long as they are not repeated.

Cultural Change

Ideally, culture and strategies being pursued will complement each other, and, again, ideally the organisation will be flexible and adaptable to change when it is appropriate. But these ideals will not always be achieved.

The culture of an organisation can be changed but it may not be easy. We need to recognise, right from the start, that this is an issue that continues to be the focus of heated debate. Many management 'gurus' take it as read that culture change is a necessary part of improving organisational effectiveness, and by implication, not a difficult thing to do. Georgiades and Macdonell[15] refer to Weick[20] who stated that organisations don't have cultures, they are cultures; and that is why they are so difficult to change.

Other researchers, particularly those who search for ways of controlling and improving organisational management, are generally more hopeful without suggesting that the task of affecting culture change is an easy one. If we see culture as being the 'glue' that holds the human organisation together, then change is guaranteed not to be easy.

If an organisation is in real difficulty, and the threat to its survival is clearly recognised, behaviour can be changed through fear and necessity. However, people may not feel comfortable and committed to the changes they accept. Behaviours may change, but not attitudes and beliefs.

The potential for changing culture is affected by:

- the strength and history of the existing culture
- how well the culture is understood

- the personality and beliefs of the strategic leader
- the extent of the strategic need

The first step in changing culture is recognising and diagnosing the existing culture, highlighting any weaknesses and stressing the magnitude of the need for change. Cultures based on fear and mistrust, on control and helplessness are cultures which will induce self protection. These cultures tend to be bureaucratic, not very creative, information does not flow quickly and there is widespread managerial emphasis on command and control.

Georgiades and Macdonell[15] refer to Kilman et al[21] who suggest that an adaptive culture is a preferable contrast, and describe it in this way: *An adaptive culture is one which entails a risk taking, trusting and proactive approach to organisational life. Members actively support one another's efforts to identify problems and implement workable solutions.*

There is a shared feeling of confidence, members believe that they can effectively manage whatever the problems and opportunities which come their way. There is widespread enthusiasm, a spirit of doing whatever it takes to achieve organisational success. The members are receptive of change and innovation.

An adaptive culture, it has been suggested, is based upon at least six core values and beliefs. Whether this is an accurate number can only be decided on the basis of personal experience.[15]

The following however take account of the majority of the variance:

1. Open and trusting relationship

Unless the organisation is characterised by relationships based on trust, in which people may speak their minds openly without fear and retribution, and in which the concerns of critical stakeholders can be freely debated and issues resolved, there seems little possibility of creating a culture of adaptation.

2. A commitment to people

No organisation seeking to renew, adapt and respond to a changing turbulent environment could do so without the wholehearted and driving commitment of its people. Commitment extends beyond the employment contract. Without commitment to our people how can we commit to our customers?

3. Participation in problem solving
Adaptive cultures require that a group of work people combine together in imaginative problem solving. Individuals require a sense of belonging to a group that has some control over its future and in which their views can at the very least be heard.

4. A commitment to change and innovation
The drive to create an adaptive culture is founded on the need for that rapid response. A core value dedicated explicitly to that commitment to change and to innovate change is thus self evident. To declare that an organisation is not dedicated to the status quo and is constantly pressing for improvement and change, is an important step in the commitment process.

5. A commitment to individual autonomy
Each individual is provided with, and committed to, a vision of what the organisation could be, and should be given the freedom and autonomy to act in the best interest of the enterprise, without unnecessary hindrance.

6. An obsessive commitment to loyal customers
Meeting with, and gathering, systematic customer, client and consumer feedback is the first requirement of this core value. Acting non defensively and then responding constructively to that feedback is the second requirement. Allowing all levels within the business to gather both data and then act upon it, within their own sphere of activity is certainly the third.

Finally, resistance to change should always be expected. People may simply be afraid because they do not understand all the reasons behind the proposed changes. They mistrust colleagues or management because of previous experiences; communications may be poor; motivation and commitment may be missing; internal architecture may be weak, causing internal conflict and hostility; and the organisation may simply not be good at sharing best practice and learning.

It is important to emphasise that, more often than not, a sizeable organisation will not have a 'single cohesive culture', if we assume that a single culture implies that the same views and behaviours are shared by most employees. Instead, the various divisions and businesses will be in some way different. The same can apply with different functional departments. Ideally, however, the most critical aspects will be shared and consistent.

Chapter 6 – Key Points

- Culture is significant and applies to the dental laboratory because it conveys a sense of identity and unity of purpose to staff.
- The success of any dental laboratory in responding to change pressures and managing the process of change is highly dependent on the values and commitment of its staff.
- Culture is vitally important and not easily changed.
- The ability of an organisation to learn, and to adopt and incrementally change strategies is dependent on politics, power, and culture.
- Culture defines how things happen inside organisations, the decisions people take and the actions they follow. Behaviour is often affected unconsciously as people simply accept 'this is the way things are done in this organisation'.
- The culture can be best understood by considering its manifestations, including values and behaviours, people and communication.
- Cultural change is difficult and takes time. Effective leadership is a fundamental requirement. People are invariably resistant to change.
- Both strategic choice and strategy implementation are affected.
- The selection and implementation of strategies reflects internal and external power and influence. We need to understand how people acquire and use power to drive decision making.
- The term re-organisational politics describes the use of power and influence. Used in the best interests of the organisation, politics is positive and an important skill for every manager. It is also necessary to appreciate that some politically astute managers will seek to manipulate situations and decisions for their own personal benefit rather than the long term needs of the organisation.
- Organisations with more adaptive cultures are able to initiate change in strategies more readily and effectively.
- It is realistic to suggest that all modes of strategy creation can be found in an organisation at any time, driven by strategic leadership, culture and power. Managers in different parts of an organisation will have different perspectives and opinions.

Chapter 7

PLANNING AND IMPLEMENTING CHANGE IN A DENTAL LABORATORY

An overview

The key purpose of this chapter is to suggest methods and processes that will help dental laboratory managers plan, create and implement strategic change within a dental laboratory environment. Planning and managing strategic change in a dental laboratory should be undertaken using a systematic, analytical approach which reviews the laboratory service as a whole in relation to its environment. This has two major functions:

1. To develop an integrated, coordinated and consistent view of the route the laboratory service wishes to follow in order to provide an efficient high standard of service for customers and patients.
2. To facilitate adaptation of the laboratory to environmental change.

At a simple structural level there is often an understanding that work has to be managed, that someone has to make decisions, and that the dental laboratory/department and the individual jobs within it depend on management functions being performed. Strategic management is concerned with understanding, as well as choosing and implementing, the strategies that a dental laboratory follows.

Dental laboratory managers should be aware of the issues and questions which must be addressed if changes in strategy are to be formulated and implemented effectively.

The management of change is an area of conflict because of the inherent issues of understanding and communication. Management actions to facilitate change can easily be misunderstood because the operational procedures and management systems already in existence appear to be working well. These days management of change is the most important management skill because it can be seen as a constant process of introducing working methods to meet changing circumstances. Successful change requires changing current management systems, operational procedures, attitudes, and the implementation of the required changes. Change requires the development of organisational and personal capabilities and appropriate timescales that will allow change to take place.

Successful management of change requires objectives which are long term, simple and agreed, an understanding of the requirements of the customer and competitive environment and an objective appraisal of the available resources.

Managing change is essentially about people and not concepts and ideas. All change involves staff and their working patterns and it can be argued that change can only be introduced at the speed at which staff are willing and able to change. Fundamental changes in attitudes take years rather than months, and the first part of the process is a clear understanding that the status quo is no longer possible. This may be through dissatisfaction with the present position or fear of the consequences of adhering to it.

For example, if external competition could clearly affect the viability of the dental laboratory service then the present position can be seen as a threat and the need for change will be more easily appreciated.

Change can also threaten the efficiency of the laboratory. Sometimes staff will resist change because they object to its content or the way in which it is carried out. The standards and beliefs of staff are important factors that will ensure the service operates to high levels of quality and efficiency. Change therefore needs to be planned and managed since the effective provision of a customer based service demands the goodwill, competence and co-operation of all staff.

Armstrong[22] refers to the work of Mintzberg[23], who believed that strategy formulation is not a rational and continuous process. He thought that, rather than being consciously and systematically developed, strategy re-orientations happen in brief quantum loops. He also suggested that:

> *"...the very concept of strategy is rooted in stability not change. Organisations pursue strategies to set directions, lay out courses of action and elicit co-operation from their members around common ground and established guidelines. By any definition, strategy imposes stability on an organisation. No stability means no strategy (no concern for the future, no pattern for the past). Indeed the mere fact of having a strategy and especially of making it explicit creates resistance to change".*

Strategies, according to Mintzberg, are not always deliberate. In theory, he says, strategy is a systematic process: '...first we think, then we act. We formulate then we implement'. In practice, '...a realised strategy can emerge in response to an evolving situation'.

The strategist can often be an organiser, a learner who manages the process in which strategies (and visions) can emerge as well as being deliberately conceived. To manage strategy is not so much to promote change as to know when to do so.

Modern dental laboratory managers are faced with a situation in which change is the only constant on which they can rely. One certainty is that working practises will not remain the same from year to year. The difficulty is deciding what these changes will be, and it can be argued that it is only by planning that the nature of such changes can be fully charted and understood. In fact managers take into account possible changes in the form of contingency plans. This is part of the process of turning dental laboratory strategic plans into detailed plans of action. While the strategic plan sets the expected, proposed and desired direction and the objectives to be achieved, this has to be translated into activity which can be implemented and controlled.

Strategy has to be developed into small action plans to be carried out by staff so that, taken together, they achieve the objectives established by the strategic plan. Much of this process is aimed at institutionalising the strategy so that it becomes part of the day-to-day work of the laboratory. Formal strategic planning systems are most useful in stable conditions. Environmental opportunities and threats are forecast, and then strategies are planned and implemented. Strategies which are appropriate, feasible and desirable are most likely to help the laboratory achieve its mission and objectives.

Where the environment is more turbulent and less predictable (i.e. the commercial sector), strategic success requires flexibility, and the ability to learn about new opportunities and introduce appropriate changes continuously.

Planning systems can still make a valuable contribution but the plans themselves must not be inflexible. During implementation it is quite likely that some plans will become discarded and others modified.

In addition, it is important not to discount the contribution of visionary strategic leaders who become aware of opportunities, on occasion create new opportunities, and take risks based on their awareness and insight of markets and customers.

Vision, mission and principles

The planning process should start with a vision and a mission, from which is derived the dental laboratory's values/principles, culture, and overall objectives and goals. This is shown in Figure 12.

It is the initial vision that both prompts and justifies change. It has also shown that this vision will continue to guide and act as a reference point throughout the change process. It is not concerned with the details of the process but touches on every aspect of change: its causes, the ultimate objective and the broad outline of the action needing to be taken.

The definition of the vision must be based on a profound understanding of the requirements of the dental laboratory service and its environment. The vision will in fact be used by dental laboratory managers as a landmark by which to steer the process of change and ensure its successful implementation and outcome.

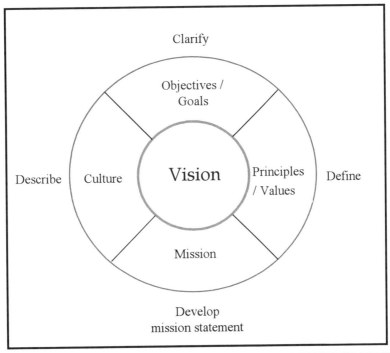

Figure 12: *Dental laboratory vision and mission*

The mission and vision statements should describe the laboratory's aspirations and additionally recognise the laboratory's responsibilities to its stakeholders. These should be further demonstrated to staff in a document outlining the laboratory's principles and culture.

It is important to note that sometimes visions fail because, from the very outset, they are too ambitious or unrealistic.

Figure 13 can be used to demonstrate how the vision and mission are linked in strategy alignment.

Dental laboratory managers must not understate the importance of forming and using a mission statement. The vision must stand on its own as a source of inspiration and direction. A mission statement is a complementary statement, much less visionary but of value in shaping the laboratory's future. A mission is the link between vision and strategy. While strategic decisions are made in order to achieve objectives, both objectives and strategy are themselves constrained by the laboratory's mission.

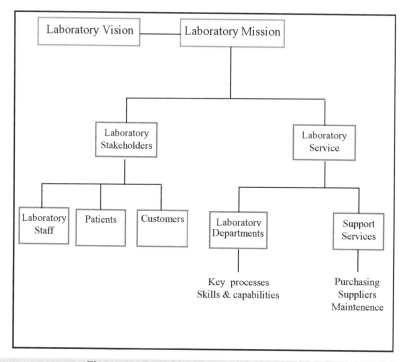

Figure 13: *Dental laboratory strategy alignment*

The laboratory's mission must, in the first instance, identify the needs and requirements of the clinical staff and more importantly the customer and the patient. The mission then should include:

- the service to customers
- the involvement of staff
- the continued improvement in the quality of service

Suggested formats for a dental laboratory's vision and mission statements and principles and culture document are:

Dental laboratory vision

To be a successful provider of high quality dental appliances through the continued development of resources and improvement in the standard of service to our customers.

Dental laboratory mission statement

To empower staff to continue to provide an excellent standard of service to customers and patients which requires upholding laboratory princi-

ples for the benefit of all stakeholders involved in the laboratory enabling it to achieve our vision.

Dental laboratory principles

Customer service – *The laboratory is committed to developing a good working relationship with customers to help the laboratory provide excellent standards of service and patient satisfaction.*
Dental laboratory staff – *We employ the best people who work as a team, are committed and enthusiastic and are valued for what they achieve and their contribution to the laboratory.*
Resources – *The laboratory provides staff with a first class working environment and supports them with continuous career development, training and up-to-date equipment and materials.*
Service and products – *The laboratory provides a reliable service and offers a wide range of high quality dental appliances.*
Leadership – *We empower all members of the team to achieve the laboratory's objectives through clear direction, support and accountability.*
Suppliers – *The laboratory is committed to developing a long term relationship which benefits both parties.*

Dental laboratory culture

Accountability – *Taking full responsibility for the results of our actions.*
Care – *Being responsive and sensitive to the needs of the patient.*
Quality – *Producing a consistent and reliable service and always striving to improve on the previous best performance.*
Communication – *Promoting open communication throughout the laboratory and recognising the importance of two-way communication.*

Planning process

Dental laboratory managers have to develop plans at the appropriate level in order to produce the actions required on a day to day basis to implement the strategic plan. Each functional/

departmental area of the laboratory will need a plan to guide its decisions and actions. This may involve market research into customer needs, or pilot promotions to test customer response. At the same time managers will have to ensure that the products and service are adapted for the market and available for the expected customer demand.

All the dental laboratory departmental plans have to be drawn together so that they operate together smoothly in supporting each other. In large laboratories, for example, the importance of this co-ordination is taken to the point of establishing a separate laboratory planning team whose role is to ensure that all the various departmental plans do fit together and support each other both in operation and in time. Where there is no such team, planning will usually be the responsibility of the dental laboratory manager.

Plans are usually developed to last for a relatively short period and they are then updated and possibly changed dramatically. However they are designed over time. Managers will also produce policies and procedures which establish the boundary lines for making decisions. These policies provide a framework for action, and a reference point for employees in their actions. For example, it may become necessary for staff to receive training in the use of new materials or equipment. Policies are created in order to meet the objectives of the laboratory and should, with other plans, help in the implementation of the strategic plan.

Ideally any documented plan will be seen as a set of intentions and guidelines, and it will be flexible. Changes to competitive and functional strategies can be made as new issues emerge. Managers are empowered to make changes within their budgets and the laboratory policy guidelines. Budgetary constraints may affect the scope of any proposed changes.

Planning systems[7]

The basic principle underpinning any planning system is:

Thinking and ideas   ⟶   Plans and budgets

Managers should seek to widen their awareness of the current situation and prepare for the challenges ahead. The challenges are both external and internal. It is essential to allow enough time and opportunity to evaluate the issues properly. It is also vital to ensure thinking continues after plans and budgets are drawn up. Plans are, after all, primarily a framework for guidance.[7]

Dental laboratories should develop systems which are appropriate for their needs. The culture and the expectations of the manager/strategic leader and the key stakeholders influence the whole process of analysis and decision making. The thinking starts with an assessment of the current position of the laboratory, its skills and resources, and an evaluation of whether there is a clear understanding of the mission, the broad objectives and directions for the future.

Then the dental laboratory environment is analysed thoroughly, concentrating on the service and products in which it currently competes and those in which it might apply its skills and resources in the future. This environmental analysis should focus on any strategic issues and current or forthcoming developments, inside or outside the laboratory, which will impact upon the ability of the laboratory to pursue its mission and meet its objectives. Ideally, these would relate to the laboratory's strengths. Potential threats should be turned into competitive opportunities.

Thompson[7] refers to Hamel[24], who argues that forward looking organisations will periodically (say every three years) bring together and cross-fertilise ideas and opinions from all parts of the organisation. The focus is on core competencies with attempts made to integrate the various businesses and divisions rather than keep them separate, as companies often do.

The emphasis must clearly be on strategic issues and on breaking down any barriers created by the structure of the dental laboratory. Amalgamation of functional and competitive strategies constitute the laboratory strategy for the future, which in turn needs to be broken down into resource development and decisions relating to changes in the structure of the laboratory, i.e. decisions which reflect where the laboratory is going and how the changes are to be managed.

The planning and implementation of strategies can be conducted without using any formal processes, but a comprehensive approach in the shape of strategic planning can insure that all the factors are taken into consideration.

Having determined the dental laboratory's objectives by setting out its vision and mission, the next key element vital in implementing sustainable strategic change is defining the need for change by diagnosing the laboratory's capability to introduce the kind of changes which will improve the service and, importantly, meet the customer's requirements.

Strategic awareness consists of the following processes:

1. *Environmental analysis* – Where are the dental laboratory's future opportunities and threats? How can it capitalise on its strengths and reduce its weaknesses.
2. *Analysing existing strategies* – Are they relevant to the environmental analysis? Where is the laboratory doing well, or badly, and why?
3. *Defining the strategic issues* – In light of the laboratory service analysis, what are the key issues the laboratory has to address in developing its strategic plan? These may include:
   a) Where does it want to go and what future objectives are realistic?
   b) Can the laboratory improve with its existing service and products?
   c) What can/cannot, should/should not the laboratory do?
   d) What are the effective criteria for change?

e) How might the change be managed?
4. *Planning and implementation* – How can the strategies be planned and implemented? Who will be involved?
5. *Monitoring* – How will the results and feedback be monitored against the objectives and plans? What methods will be used for taking corrective action?

Figure 14 can be used by laboratory managers to demonstrate these processes.

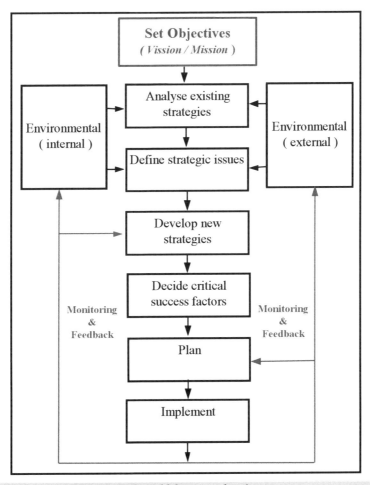

Figure 14: *Dental laboratory planning process*

Analysing the dental laboratory service

Dental laboratory managers have to introduce change to the service extensively across all aspects of the structure, systems and people if the strategic change is to be lasting and successful. Putting in place an effective strategy means:

1. Identifying what the customers expect from the laboratory service in the future and how their changing needs can be satisfied.
2. Assessing the laboratory's strengths and weaknesses in relation to its existing organisational capability i.e. products, current staffing and skill levels, operational systems and structure. Determining what opportunities there are for exploiting its strengths.
3. Deciding whether the present resources, systems and structure will enable the objectives to be achieved.
4. Identifying the problems and translating them into the agenda for change – the strategic plan.

This analysis should take place within the clear framework of direction and purpose as represented in the dental laboratory's vision and mission which is linked to the laboratory's overall strategic plan.

As previously discussed in Chapter 3, a SWOT analysis is a useful method of clarifying the current strategic situation and is arguably more valuable when used as a basis for projecting forward.

The dilemma for managers is how to introduce change which will alleviate the problems highlighted in the study. For example, demand for increased production while maintaining standards, variations in workload, patient expectations, and the on-going changes within dentistry. It would be useful for managers to use the model suggested in Figure 3 to help them understand the link between these three key areas and analyse the laboratory's ability to change by building a picture of the service present, how it should operate in the future, and what is the agenda that will create that change. It will also help pinpoint which aspects of the service fit the plan for strategic change and which aspects will themselves need to be changed to achieve the desired objectives.

Figure 15 may help managers understand and be aware of the present situation and determine what is required for implementing, managing and sustaining strategic change. Without the organisational capability to make change happen then there can be no deliverable strategy for change.

From the analysis, dental laboratory managers must decide on the extent and type of strategic change that is required. Listing criteria for strategic choice is a suggested approach. A number of these may require further analysis to be undertaken. For example,

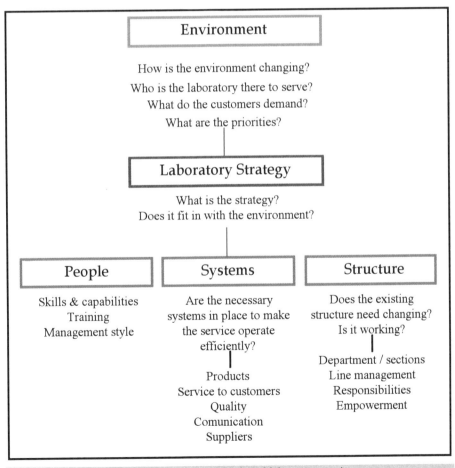

Figure 15: *Analysing the dental laboratory service*

the consequences of the strategy failing or the consequences of the customers' reactions.

Strategies that minimise organisational or strategic change are preferable to those requiring greater change, provided that the resulting strategic choice will meet the laboratory's objectives. In general the simpler the overall approach the better.

In order to minimise change the first issue is whether continuing with the present strategy will achieve the laboratory's objectives outlined in its vision and mission.

Laboratory managers could be faced with the following scenarios:

- If the present strategy does appear to be appropriate, then the next step is to ensure that the laboratory will have, or can acquire the resources necessary either to successfully maintain or improve efficiency and quality of service. If the analysis then reveals that not only is the current strategy still appropriate but the laboratory is capable of any necessary adaptations to the service, then a major review of strategy is not urgent and attention can turn to improving performance further using the results of the SWOT findings. It may, however, be desirable to set more ambitious targets/objectives and improve the overall performance accordingly or perhaps alter the dental laboratory's mission in the light of the findings.

2. If the strategy either:
   a) will not work in the future because environmental changes have made it inappropriate; or
   b) cannot work because internally, the laboratory is incapable of adapting to the requirements of the strategy, i.e. the weaknesses cannot be overcome, then a new or modified strategy is clearly necessary and, preferably, should be based on existing strengths since this will minimise major internal changes.

3. If, however, the analysis suggests that:
   a) existing strengths are inadequate to meet the objectives, cannot fully take advantage of an opportunity, or meet a threat that jeopardises improvement in the efficiency of the service; or

b) existing weaknesses, which are the reason for the inadequacies in the service, cannot be overcome, then a more fundamental change may be needed. This may imply a major input of resources (mainly financial).

In order for laboratory managers to make a choice between the number of alternative strategies, there must be criteria against which they can be evaluated. Suggested criteria for choosing suitable strategies are:

a) How well does it contribute to the laboratory's objectives?
b) Is the strategy consistent with the laboratory's policies/culture?
c) Does the strategy overcome the strategic weaknesses and counter the environmental threats?
d) What would be the consequences of the strategy failing or being a partial success?
e) Is the strategy feasible and what are the potential rewards?
f) What will the stakeholders' (customers/patients) requirements be?

Implementing change

Change programmes must be fully comprehensive if they are to last and be successful. From their analysis, dental laboratory managers, as strategic leaders, should identify the key areas which require change, have most impact, and then focus attention more widely as the laboratory activities are interdependent and should not be approached in isolation, i.e. the changes can affect other areas, for example, suppliers.
Having fully examined the priorities and proposed changes, managers must ensure that sufficient time and resources are available to implement the changes.

The appropriate process for implementing change within the laboratory will depend on a number of factors such as urgency, culture management/leadership style and the degree of autonomy given to the manager. For example, the need to consult and seek approval from third parties who will be directly or indirectly affected by the change.

From the analysis of the laboratory service, the laboratory manager should be able to determine appropriate, feasible and desirable areas for strategic/organisational change which will form the framework of the laboratory's mission. He/she must also ensure that the laboratory is able to maintain and manage existing services efficiently and effectively during the change process. Figure 16 shows a suitable model for implementing a change programme within a laboratory. A planning team, headed by the laboratory manager is formed and team leaders are selected from the departmental sections who will then prepare plans for their individual areas in consultation with their team members. The dental laboratory manager then reviews the plans to ensure the proposals align with the laboratory's overall objectives and the plans are refined through discussion with departmental/section leaders. Training and development needs are identified at this time.

The agreed plans should be reviewed by the planning team to ensure that the plan meets with, and can be incorporated in, the laboratory's overall strategic plan.

The changes that have been introduced should be monitored closely and corrective action taken when necessary. The plan is reviewed at the end of the agreed period. The outcome in terms of the laboratory's strategic management and organisational success will be dependent on:

a) the direction provided by the manager as strategic leader
b) the culture of the laboratory
c) the extent to which the department/section/team leaders and staff within the laboratory understand, support and own the laboratory's vision, mission and strategy, and appreciate the significance of their individual contribution.
d) the effectiveness of the communication/information, monitoring and control systems.

Implementation of the planned changes incorporates a number of aspects, some of which can be changed directly and others

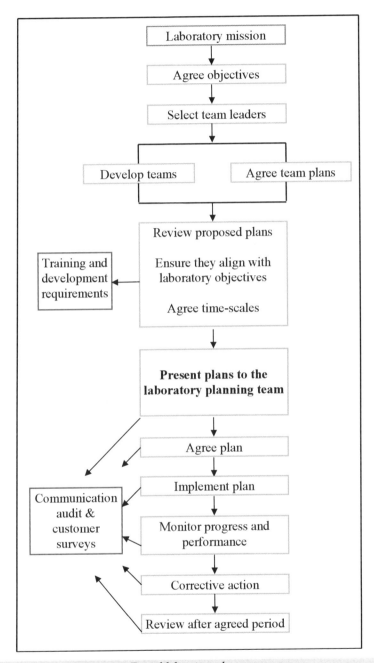

Figure 16: *Dental laboratory change programme*

indirectly. The latter are more difficult for the manager to control and change. Aspects of implementation which can be changed directly are:

1. Laboratory structure (the actual defined organisational structure)
2. Service delivery
3. Activity targets
4. Management systems
5. Operational policies and procedures
6. Management information systems
7. Action plans

Actions of implementation which are changed indirectly are:

a) *Communication systems* – adequate communication systems help determine the awareness of change. Such communication is affected and influenced by the degree of co-operation between managers, team leaders and staff. Problems in communication can result in the change not being monitored correctly and resistance from those affected by the change.
b) *Managing and developing quality and excellence* – attention to detail, delivery of the service on time (and to the appropriate quality), and the personal development and training of all managers and staff are all factors of this. As well as developing management skills it is also important to develop the knowledge and skills of technical staff.
c) *Laboratory culture* – This involves the way things are done, standards and attitudes which are held and practised.
d) *Fostering of innovation* – The willingness of people to search for improvements and better ways of doing things. Encouragement and reward is important and is very much influenced by the strategic leader.

To ensure successful implementation of planned changes the following areas must therefore be addressed by the laboratory manager:

1. The necessary actions required to implement the changes should be identified and planned and clear responsibility for the successful outcome of the strategic/organisational change should be allocated.

2. The number of strategies and changes pursued at any time should be limited.
3. Appropriate timescales and processes for monitoring progress and performance should be established.
4. The availability of necessary and adequate resources to cope with the changes should be seen as a key determinant of the strategy and not be overlooked.
5. The involvement and support of people who will be affected by the changes must be considered and the implications of the proposed changes should be communicated widely, awareness created and commitment and involvement sought. Encouragement, incentives/reward systems can help this.
6. The style of leadership will be influential. The structure of the laboratory, delegation of responsibilities, the freedom of team leaders to act, their willingness to exercise initiative and incentives will all be determined and influenced by the leader. These in turn determine the effectiveness of the implementation. The manager's choices and autonomy may be influenced/constrained by environmental forces and resource limitations.
7. The timing of when to act and make changes is also important in reducing resistance to change.

Implementation and the organisational structure

The prospects for effective implementation are clearly dependent on the appropriateness, feasibility and desirability of the strategy. Some strategies are not capable of implementation. At the same time, competency in implementation (the ability to translate ideas into actions and generate positive outcomes) can itself be a source of competitive advantage. Internal processes can add value by creating high levels of customer service and/or saving on costs by, for instance, removing any unnecessary delays or duplication of activities.

Thompson[25] refers to Reed and Buckley[26], who suggest that new strategies are selected because they offer opportunities and potential benefits, but that their implementation, because it involves change, implies risk. Implementation strategies should seek to maximise benefits and minimise risks.

The major implementation themes concern organisational structures, policies and control systems related to management of resources, and the management of strategic change[25].

The fundamental questions for dental laboratories are as follows:

- How appropriate is the laboratory's structure, given the diversity of the strategic perspective and the inter-relationships between various departments, products and services?
- How effectively are we managing our resources? Are the various departments and activities co-ordinated and contributing towards clearly understood objectives?

This last question relates to both implementation and control, and the ability to answer it is determined by the effectiveness of the information system and strategic awareness of managers. Strategy implementation requires the deployment and control of the laboratory's strategic resources to carry out action plans and hopefully achieve target milestones.

The strategic resources include finance, technology, people, information, and products, services and their distribution. This is accomplished through the design of the organisation (structure) and the process encapsulated within the structure. It is also important that progress is monitored and changes introduced when necessary.[7]

The structure must therefore be capable of implementing strategies, and it can be described as the *means by* which an organisation seeks to achieve its strategic objectives. However, we also saw in Chapter 6 that the structural processes are a reflection of culture, power and political activity, and that people are empowered in a decentralised organisation. It is these processes which determine the actual adaptive/incremental strategies that are pursued. Consequently the structure must be capable of both formulating and implementing strategy.

A simple circular relationship could be shown as:

Implementing process

Strategy ──────────────────────► **Structure**

Creation Process

This relationship is expanded in Figure 17.

Figure 17 emphasises that, first, the strategy process involves awareness, ideas for change and implementation, and, second, the process is driven by culture, power and politics.

Plans and targets are derived from intended strategies; they comprise what people *should do*. The decisions people take and

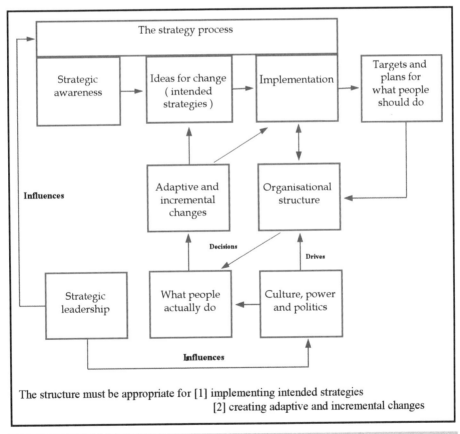

Figure 17: *Strategy→Structure; Structure→Strategy*[7]

carry out within the structure (what they *actually do*) result in adaptive and incremental change.

Organisational structure

Buchanan and Huczynski[14] refer to Child[27] who stresses that:

"The allocation of responsibilities, the grouping of functions, decision making, co-ordination, control and reward — all these are fundamental requirements for the continued operation of an organisation. The quality of an organisation's structure will affect how well these requirements are met."

They also refer to Drucker's[28] definition in the Harvard Business Review (January – February 1974) as:

"Structure is a means for attaining the objectives and goals of an organisation. The extent to which and the ways in which organisation members are constrained and controlled by the organisation and the distribution of activities and responsibilities, and the organisational procedures and regulations."

These two statements refer to the perceived purpose of organisational structure.

The outcome of a company's organising activities can be depicted in organisational design. The object of the design is to create an organisational structure which fits with the objectives, its resources and its environment. The structure describes the relationship between different parts of the organisation and the people in it.[29]

Structure is clearly important for any dental laboratory whatever its size. However, in the smaller laboratories there are likely to be fewer problems of structure.

The distribution of tasks, the definition of authority and responsibilities, and the relationship between staff within the laboratory can be established on a personal and informal basis. With increasing size, however, there is greater need for a carefully designed and purposeful form of organisational structure within the laboratory. The structure of the laboratory affects not only productivity and efficiency but also morale and job satisfaction.

The structure should be depicted in the form of an organisational chart as demonstrated in the case studies.[6] This will show how tasks are divided, the grouping together of activities and the levels of authority. The chart provides a pictorial representation of the structural framework of the laboratory and can include additional details such as an indication of the broad nature of duties and responsibilities of the individuals and various departments, and the names/grading of employees.

The dental laboratory's structure and management systems are reorganised at the same time. As a result, employees' working methods will change, their behavioural patterns will also alter and finally, the laboratory culture will be modified. Any change programme therefore starts by redefining tasks and responsibilities. This can be brought about, for example, through training sessions, seminars and team briefing.
The following structural forms can be adapted by commercial and hospital dental laboratories when attempting to design an appropriate structure to satisfy its particular needs.

1. The entrepreneurial structure
2. The functional structure
3. Dental teaching hospital laboratory structure

1. The entrepreneurial structure
(Small commercial and hospital laboratories)

This structure, shown in Figure 18, is built around the owner/manager and typically utilised by small laboratories in the early stages of their development. The structure is totally centralised. All key decisions are made by the owner/manager, and employees refer everything significant back to him or her.

This structure is particularly useful for new commercial laboratories and small hospital laboratories as it enables the owner/manager, who normally will have some expertise with the

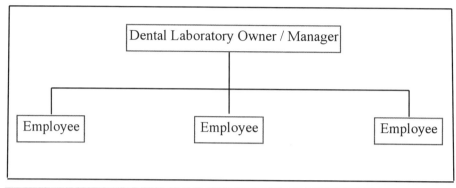

Figure 18: *The entrepreneurial structure*

product or service and whose investment is at risk (commercial sector), to control the growth and development.

There is an argument that this is not really a formal structure as all the responsibilty, power and authority lies with one person. However in some small laboratories of this nature, selected employees will specialise and be given job titles and some limited responsibility for specified activities.

2. The functional structure
(Larger commercial and hospital laboratories)

The functional structure, Figure 19, is commonplace in small commercial laboratories which have outgrown the entrepreneurial structure and in larger laboratories which produce only a limited range of related products and services.

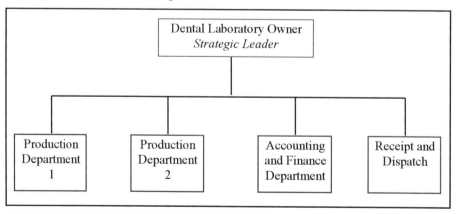

Figure 19: *The functional structure*

This structure is also a typical internal structure of the divisions and business units which comprise larger diversified companies. It is more suitable in a stable environment than a turbulent one as it is generally centralised with company and competitive strategies, again being controlled by a strategic leader.[25]

The structure is built around the tasks to be carried out, which tend to be split into specialist functional areas. Managers are placed in charge of departments which are responsible for those functions, and they may well have delegated authority to change functional strategies. Consequently the effectiveness of this structure is very dependent on the ability of these specialist managers to work together as a team and support each other, and on a strategic leader to co-ordinate their efforts.

Functional managers will develop valuable specialist expertise and the relatively simple lines of communication between these specialists and their strategic leader can facilitate a high degree of strategic awareness.

Dental teaching hospital structure

The introduction of self governing NHS Trusts enabled all hospitals and other units to take greater responsibility for their own affairs, so the people providing the services were making the decisions. There was a devolution of budgetary control and responsibility.[6] The change to Trust status involved hospitals introducing new organisational frameworks and management structures which would affect how well the Trust's requirements were met. The correct design of these structures is important, particularly when organisational and/or strategic change is being planned and introduced. The structures that were developed aimed for the maximum amount of delegation possible in the way services were provided, both in the organisational structure and in financial management, subject to the overall responsibility of the Trust Board in statutory matters and in terms of public accountability. Trust Boards dealt mainly with the issues of major strategy affecting the Trust as a whole and focused on major national issues.

Most Trusts are characterised by a decentralised organisational structure based on a number of clinical and service Directorates or associated hospitals acting, as far as possible, as natural business units. In addition, there is a small central core of non-clinical Directorates which provide services to all the clinical and other Directorates, together with the corporate leadership and co-ordination that is required to maintain and improve the coherence of such a highly complex organisation.

Some dental hospitals became Trust hospitals, although the majority became Directorates of a larger Trust, with substantially devolved managerial and financial power. They were empowered to develop strategic and business plans for their Directorate and to be responsible for the internal management of all the services.

Dental hospitals became either Directorates or Trusts. All Direct Managed Units became a Directorate or Trust hospital by the end of 1997 (Figure 20). Some Dental Schools were incorporated into the organisational structure of the Trust hospital or Directorate, with a common managerial structure, to form a Dental Institute).

NB: As discussed in Chapter 1, the majority of Trust hospitals have now become Foundation Trust Hospitals.

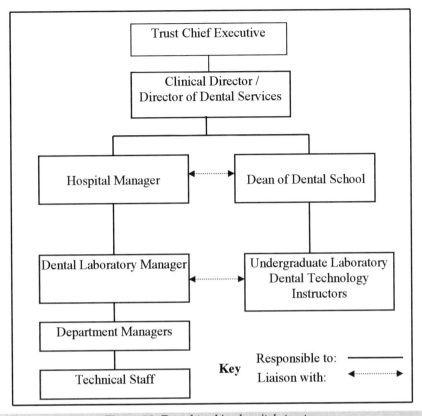

Figure 20: *Dental teaching hospital structure*

Chapter 7 – Key points

- Planning is vital for thinking and learning about future strategic issues, challenges and opportunities.
- The actual process of thinking and planning is more important than the plan itself, which really should be seen as a framework for guidance
- The overall strategic plan is developed from functional/departmental plans which include the tasks for employees to carry out.
- The planning process includes the development of plans at departmental level.
- The plans and actions of functional departments need to be drawn together so that the laboratory operates smoothly.
- Plans establish how laboratories intend to change to meet the requirements of their customers.
- Organisational development can help managers deal with changes through staff training and development, team building and internal communication.
- Strategic objectives can be implemented by processes such as management by objectives and performance related pay. These systems focus on individual objectives and feedback on their achievement.
- Strategic management comprises analysis choice and implementation. Strategies are implemented through the organisational structure. However, the structural processes are the determinants of adaptive and incremental changes. As a result there is a circular relationship between strategy and structure.
- Effective control is achieved when strategy and structure are matched and are also congruent with the style of laboratory management. Simultaneous change to these three, what has been earlier termed strategic regeneration, is difficult, but sometimes necessary for laboratories.
- Structures are designed to separate the activities and tasks which the laboratory must carry out.
- There are a variety of organisational structures which help to achieve the strategic objectives of a laboratory. Without these structures, actions that will achieve these objectives and ensure the quality of products and services provided cannot be taken.
- Dental laboratories are likely to conform, either closely or loosely to one of three identifiable structural forms: The entrepreneurial structure, functional structure, and hospital structure.

Chapter 8

QUALITY MANAGEMENT WITHIN A DENTAL LABORATORY AND THE CUSTOMER

Quality management

Quality can be defined as **'continually meeting agreed customer needs – getting it right first time'**.

A large number of hospital and commercial laboratories have already introduced quality management systems based on British Standard 5750 or its international counterpart ISO 9002. These standards do not establish a level of excellence for a product or service but they do provide **'a way of describing the capability of a system to produce products or services to a specification'**.[4]

Quality within a dental laboratory falls into two categories: Firstly, the quality of the service provided, which is determined by the management systems and operational procedures that are in place, based on the customer's requirements. Secondly, the quality of the product that is produced. This is also determined by the working procedures that are in place and the customer's requirements.

"Total quality management" is a long term strategy and it is about the management of change and involves all aspects of human resource management, and effective and efficient control of resources and training. This style of management is participative and is designed to enable managers at every level to make decisions and be responsible for them. This means devolving decision making to the closest possible point where the effects of the decisions are felt.

Improving the quality of the way activities are managed and carried out in dental laboratories invariably leads to lower costs through less waste and through 'getting it right first time', the central theme of total quality management. Successful laboratories will also strive to 'get it right' every time. Reputations for good quality are quickly lost when customers relate stories of poor experiences.

The expression *total quality management* therefore relates to everything which happens in a laboratory and which can lead to lower costs and, particularly, the improvement of customer service. The speed of response to queries, the way in which telephone calls are dealt with, accurate delivery notes and invoices are all examples outside the direct production activity.

Thompson[25] quotes Georg Karnsund, President, Saab-Scania AB, whose definition of quality is:

> *"Quality is not a label you can put on a product afterwards. Quality is a way of life that must apply to everything within the company and all its external relations. Quality is in essence a question of leadership. Only a minor part of errors are attributable to the shop floor. Quality is created by the attitude and action of management. It is something that must be part of corporate objectives and strategies."*

In satisfying customer needs, dental laboratories should seek to improve the quality of their operations in terms of people, systems and technology. Improving people can be relatively inexpensive, but it requires that they are seen and treated as a key resource. Training and development is essential, and the ways in which employees might improve the quality of their individual contribution should be discussed with them.

Most people know how they could perform more effectively, but quite often they are never asked. Systems should reflect clear policies and standards and communication systems should keep people aware of how well or badly the company is doing at any time. Technology can improve quality through increased productivity and through eliminating human error, but it can be very expensive.

Total quality management should start with the strategic leader who must emphasise a commitment to it, but it must also spread throughout the company. Everybody in the organisation is responsible for quality. The philosophy that prevention (getting things right first time) is better than detection (correcting complaints) must be seen as a priority.

Thompson[25] refers to PA Consultants[30], who contend that companies which have pursued total quality have been able to benefit in a number of ways. Specifically they have:

- improved the company image
- improved productivity
- reduced costs
- created greater certainty in their operations (by reducing conflicts within the operating system they have improved the speed of delivery and their flexibility in responding to changes in customer requirements)
- improved morale (employees have shown greater concern and commitment where they have seen that there is an emphasis on things being done well and that high standards have been encouraged, valued and rewarded)
- committed customers

Thompson[25] also refers to Peters[31], who argues that, if an organisation is committed to total quality management, there are a number of issues which must be addressed. These are:

1. The necessary commitment to getting things right first time must be encouraged and developed throughout the organisation.
2. Employees must be trained about how they can measure quality and quality improvements.
3. There must be a guiding system or ideology stemming from the strategic leader; continual improvements must be managed.
4. There need to be clear targets and measures of success. Numbers of rejects, repeats and returns from customers are all examples, and the results should be communicated.
6. Quality improvements should be rewarded, as should new ideas for improvement.
6. Quality issues should be communicated laterally throughout the organisation as problems can span several areas of the business.

7. Relationships with customers and suppliers should be developed. The organisation is seeking to meet the requirements of their customers; suppliers should be seeking to meet the requirements and needs of the organisation.

These issues are all linked in a chain of inter-dependencies. Peters also suggests that opportunities to improve will never dry up and that organisations who seek to innovate and find new and better ways of doing things are more likely to create differentiation and reduce their costs.

The customer

Case studies[6] of private sector companies have identified the importance of customers for any organisation, and that interaction between companies and their customers has increased in the past few years and is likely to continue to do so. It has also been shown that the customer has needs which should be met by the organisation and that customer requirements are not simply concerned with the product or service provided, but also the way in which the operation is carried out and the expected effect on the customer.

Hospital and commercial dental laboratories provide an extensive service to general dental practitioners (gdps), clinical staff and undergraduate/postgraduate students. This includes a wide range of routine, complex, specialized and highly specialised prostheses. Although they do not provide this service directly to the patient, their needs and those of the clinical staff and gdps must be taken into consideration.

The dental laboratory's customers have a direct influence on performance objectives, through critical success factors: the key factors by which the customer decides whether the laboratory and its service/products are suitable for their needs. The link between them is demonstrated in Figure 21.

It is important that dental laboratory managers understand their customers in order to meet the specific requirements of each

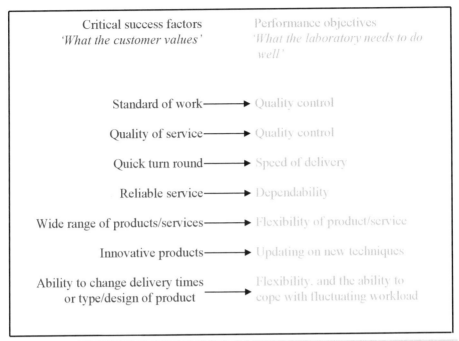

Figure 21: *Customer needs*

and whether these requirements can be segmented. If there are well defined customer segments, this can have important implications for the type of product, its design and operational procedures.

Managers in hospital laboratories do attempt to segment customer requirements in order to satisfy as many people as possible, in particular the preferential design requirements of clinical staff. The latter also applies to undergraduate students whose design requirements for some products remain consistent for teaching purposes.

At the same time all clinical staff and gdps will have different ideas and priorities in terms of standard of work and quality of service. These include design, technical preferences (materials), reliability and service delivery. Managers and technical staff need to know how important these factors are to their customers before they decide on which aspect to concentrate on improving.

In the case of commercial laboratories, price is an important factor and it is critical to know customer purchase criteria and equally critical to understand how well the laboratory meets their needs relative to its competitors. This cost factor is important to some hospital laboratories who are generating income from external customers.

Studies have shown[6] that it is generally accepted that quality of service and standard/quality of product is a measure of excellence taken from the customer's point of view. It means delivering the right product or service which is fit for the purposes required by the customer. Quality control often occurs at the end of the production process and is a method of monitoring the conformity of the product to the agreed specifications.

A concept which builds on quality control is the 'just-in-time' principle which has been adopted by some private sector companies and could be used in hospital and commercial dental laboratories. This is concerned with improving production efficiency and reducing waste. It is a technique for minimising storage of materials through careful planning and purchasing to meet the exact requirements of the customer, internal or external. This requires co-operation from suppliers.

It is at strategic management level that decisions are made about total quality management (the management and implementation of a change process which will provide the best product and service possible to meet customer needs) and systems of quality control.

The private sector companies that were studied[6] have introduced Quality Assurance frameworks for quality control and quality improvement. Quality Assurance supports the teams of employees with systems, resources and discretion appropriate to the company, to keep them in tune with progress of quality management and improvement.[6]

The concentration on customer specification has produced standard registration marks/accreditation such as BS EN ISO 9002: 1994, Medical Devices Directive (93/42/EEC) (MDD) and the Dental Appliance Manufacturers Audit Scheme (DAMAS). These standards which have been adopted by dental laboratories (and which were mandatory from June 1998 in the case of MDD) do not establish a level of excellence for a product or service, but they do provide a way of describing the capability of a system to produce products or services to a specification.

Customers should not expect these standards to make a product the best available and registration is not a necessary prerequisite to total quality management. Quality Assurance supplies the customer with written evidence, documented systems and procedures on the laboratory's effectiveness. These standards are designed to control each step in the process so that products and services match the specification. The procedures must be regularly audited to ensure they are being adhered to in detail, and form a basis for and must be taken into consideration during the planning and implementation of change.

Chapter 8 – Key Points

- Total quality management is a key organisational value which can contribute significantly towards the achievement of customer satisfaction and lower costs.
- Underlying the quest for quality is the need to increase productivity by improving technology, and by making the most of the work force. This involves delegation of decision making and responsibility in the process of achieving quality objectives. It also involves a concentration on training and development based on high expectations and increasing people's ability to deal with modern technology and participative management.
- Quality implies more than the quality of the product itself, although this is obviously important. It incorporates the dental laboratory's ability to meet the specific needs and requirements of its customers, such as delivery on time, of the right quantity and packaged appropriately.
- Improving the quality of the way activities are managed and carried out invariably leads to lower costs, less waste and, through 'getting it right first time', a central theme of total quality management.
- The focus of the strategy for all dental laboratories should be customer satisfaction. Laboratories should endeavour to achieve quality and an efficient and reliable service by changing both their own internal and external operations and relationships in order to improve their performance and meet the needs and expectations of their customers more efficiently than their competitors by giving better value.
- The introduction of 'just in time' systems which sequence operations so that products/services are delivered as and when required by the customer is an important feature of improving customer service.
- Other important factors are the adding to and/or upgrading of information technology systems. Regular feedback from customers, suppliers and employees, improved invoicing and communication and reviewing and upgrading in-house training.
- Actions to improve quality include the introduction of quality systems which comply with the requirements of approved quality standards in relation to documented work instructions, the control and monitoring of work and procedures.

Chapter 9

FACTORS AFFECTING SUCCESSFUL CHANGE IN A DENTAL LABBORATORY

Leadership

Management practices are the mechanisms through which the leadership of the dental laboratory will shape the behaviours which are appropriate for developing the culture and which drives the day to day actions and procedures that will ultimately affect both individual, section/team and overall laboratory performance.

One of the main objectives of change is to make the laboratory service more customer orientated at all levels. The delivery process will give priority to customer contact by all members of staff and an appreciation of customer needs and expectations.

The manner in which dental laboratory managers seek to introduce change has a direct and significant impact on the way change is implemented. Since changes in practice and behaviour cannot be affected by decree or by issuing orders, the way managers go about delivering change is itself the vehicle for creating the evolution to the new state of affairs.

Studies of companies have shown that effective leadership, within which vision makes a major contribution, is a critical element.[6] Too many people tend to think that responsibility for leadership is restricted to the strategic leader of the organisation (chief executive of the organisation) but this is a mistake. Leadership qualities need to be developed at all levels in the organisation.[6]

Laboratory managers as leaders can follow the examples of the type and quality of leadership adopted by managers in the private sector companies studied.[6] To be an effective leader, laboratory managers must have a clear purpose and direction, and a means to achieve that purpose. In other words he/she will provide the 'where' and the 'how'.

To be successful managers must:

- ensure that they stay informed
- want to be successful managers
- deploy their energy into making things happen
- improve and persuade others to become involved
- be responsive to change pressures
- be flexible and adaptive
- adopt the 'open door' style of leadership

Dental laboratory managers must be flexible, capable of adapting and willing to relinquish personal control. They should also ensure that the laboratory possesses the skills and competencies that will enable it to adapt and deal with the various issues and challenges it faces. Ideally managers will empower the departmental managers and encourage them to be visionary and become confident in their own abilities.

They should look at the existing strategies and perform what is called 'gap analysis'. Here they simply attempt to determine whether a performance gap exists between what their existing strategy can realistically be expected to accomplish and the objectives that have been established.

This can be in areas such as productivity, training and development, customer care and environmental issues. Where there is not a gap, then managers can assume that the current strategy is the appropriate one. Where serious gaps exist then managers will need to investigate these and look for alternative strategies. This process was particularly important, in the companies studied, if they were to remain competitive.[6]

Monitoring and reviewing

Strategic planning and implementation is not a static process. Once the framework is in place and working it needs to be reviewed in the light of any changes or problems. Laboratory managers should review all aspects of the strategic plan at frequent intervals. At one extreme the action plan requires constant monitoring and adjustment, while at the other, the mission statement may need to be altered. This should reflect the fact that while the direction of the laboratory should not be changing too frequently, the actions required to maintain that direction will entail frequent adjustment.

The monitoring and review process provides the loop back to all stages of the planning process, as shown in Figure 14 (page 73), and should provide a reminder that change and improvement are a constant feature of strategic planning. In monitoring a laboratory's strategic plan it should also be matched against its values and principles.

Revision of the change programme requires data and feedback. Once the plan has been implemented its results should be measured, and opinions and suggestions obtained from all those involved. This can be achieved through audit, customer and people (laboratory staff) surveys and product analysis.

As previously discussed, strategic change requires change in behaviour which in turn flows from and creates changes in attitude. Even if people's behaviour complies with the changes, managers must not assume that all is well; attitudes can become negative, and this can undermine morale. Regular meetings are essential to maintain good communication links and ensure that people still support the change programme, strategies and objectives; especially if these are being revised or replaced.

Human resources

Human resources are the dental laboratory's most important asset and the effective management of human resources is a key determinant of effective and efficient implementation of change and of the laboratory's success in achieving its objectives. Human resource management is much more than the application within the laboratory of a set of management techniques. It is concerned with the wider implications of management of change and not just with the effects of change on working practices. It seeks proactively to encourage flexible attitudes and the acceptance of new working practices. Human resource planning should be linked to the laboratory's objectives, strategic plan and targets. The competence and commitment of staff and the use made of skills learned should be reviewed at all levels against these objectives and targets.

The training and development needs of each member of staff should be converted into the individual department/laboratory strategic plan. Individual training and development plans should identify whether training is conducted internally or externally, and the departmental/laboratory manager should discuss with staff what the type of training is, and what the personal and laboratory objectives will be.

Ideally all staff should be appraised though an objectives based appraisal process as shown in Figure 22. Objectives agreed should always be time based, preferably over a twelve month period, which means that as each completion date arrives there is an automatic review of progress.

The main point of appraisal is to align the employee's personal objectives with those of their department and/or laboratory, and help the individuals concerned achieve their full potential. The appraisal identifies the individual strengths and areas for devel-

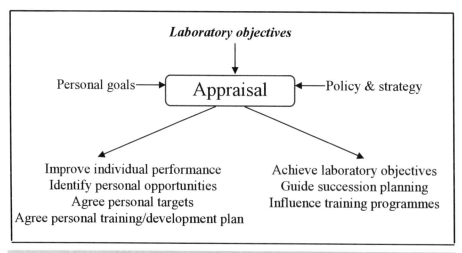

Figure 22: *Dental laboratory employee appraisal*

opment. The appraisal interview is a two way discussion on the employee's performance during the past twelve months against the agreed objectives. Managers conducting appraisals should be required to attend training in appraisal skills.

Dental laboratory culture

The popular and simple way of defining culture is: *'how things are done around here'*. A more detailed definition is *'the collection of traditions, values, policies, beliefs and attitudes that constitute a pervasive context for everything we do in an organisation'*.[22]

The culture and structure of dental laboratories have developed and will continue to develop over time in response to a complex set of factors. We can, however, identify a number of key influences that are likely to play an important role in any planned changes and development of any laboratory's culture. These include: history, primary function, technology, goals and objectives, size, location, management style and leadership, staffing and the environment.

The nature of the laboratory's 'business' and its primary function have an important influence in its culture. This includes the range and quality of products and services provided, the importance and type of customer i.e. gdps, hospital clinical staff or undergraduate students,

The primary function of the dental laboratory and the nature of the technological processes and methods will affect the structure and culture. The laboratory must give attention to its objectives in all areas of its operations. The combination of objectives and resultant strategies will influence culture and may itself be influenced by changes in culture.

Usually larger laboratories have more formalised structures and cultures. Increased size is likely to result in separate departments and split operations. This may cause difficulties in communication and inter departmental rivalries with the need for effective co-ordination. A rapid expansion, or decline, in size and resultant changes in staffing will influence structure and culture.

The location of the laboratory to its customers/clinical areas (dental hospitals) can have an influence on culture, for example whether the laboratory is near and readily accessible to customers/clinical staff. An accessible and direct link is essential to good communication and continuity in maintaining good practice and quality standards.

Laboratory managers can have a considerable influence on the nature of the laboratory's culture. However, all members of staff help to shape the dominant culture of a laboratory, irrespective of what management feel it should be. Culture is determined by the nature of staff employed and the extent to which they accept management philosophy and policies or pay only 'lip service'.

In order to be effective, the laboratory must be responsive to external environmental influences. For example, if the laboratory operates within a dynamic environment it requires a structure and culture that is sensitive and readily adaptable to change. An organic structure is more likely to respond effectively to new opportunities and challenges, and risks and limitations presented by the external environment.

Culture helps to account for variations among dental laboratories. It helps to explain why different groups of people perceive things in their own way and perform things differently from other groups.

Culture can help reduce complexity and uncertainty. It provides a consistency in outlook and values and is clearly an important ingredient of effective laboratory performance. Without exception, the dominance and coherence of culture proved to be an essential quality of the successful companies. In these companies, all the people knew what they were supposed to do in most situations because the guiding values and objectives were crystal clear.[6]

Climate

In addition to the planning and implementation of changes to the laboratory's operational procedures and management systems and structure, laboratory managers have a responsibility for creating a climate in which staff are motivated to work willingly and effectively. Laboratory climate is a general concept and difficult to define precisely. It is more something which is felt. Climate can be said to relate to the prevailing atmosphere surrounding the laboratory and the hospital, to the level of morale, and to the strength of feeling of belonging and care and goodwill among staff. It will influence the attitudes which staff in the laboratory bring to bear on their work performance and personal relationships. The extent to which staff accept the culture of the laboratory will have a significant effect on climate. It is based on the perceptions of staff towards the laboratory and/or hospital.

Climate was characterised in the companies studied by the nature of the people-organisation relationship and the management-staff relationship. These relationships were determined by the interactions among the goals, objectives, formal structure, management/leadership style and the behaviour of people. Although similar types of companies will share common features and norms, each company will have its own different and distinctive climate and culture.[6]

This will also apply to dental laboratories. A laboratory is unlikely to sustain change and attain optimum operational performance if the culture and climate does not evoke a spirit of co-operation throughout the laboratory and is not conducive to motivating staff to work willingly and effectively.

Climate will influence the level of morale and the attitudes laboratory staff bring to bear on their work performance and personal relationships. Morale, however, is another general concept which is difficult to measure objectively.

A carefully designed and conducted attitude survey, which most successful companies undertake, can help to establish the feelings of staff on factors contributing to the laboratory's climate. When morale is low, it is important that positive action is taken to remedy the causes.

Factors that influence laboratory morale

Morale can be viewed in terms of mental attitudes which staff have towards their duties and responsibilities. Before dental laboratory managers can start to improve morale they should review the main areas in which to develop the best possible attitudes in their staff.

Figure 23 shows how the interrelated states of motivation, job satisfaction and group cohesiveness can affect laboratory morale which in turn can affect the successful implementation of change. The important factors are:

Being valued – A feeling of being valued for their contribution to the success of the laboratory. Job satisfaction based on competent performance.

Team work amongst staff – A sense of group pride and self esteem, good interaction and working relations with colleagues and other members of the dental team, team effort

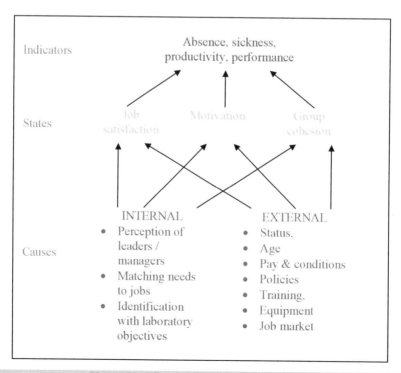

Figure 23: *Effects on dental laboratory morale*

and support of other staff including team/section leaders and manager.

Management care about staff welfare – Just reward to staff for their contribution and effort. A clear statement of management objectives, and an attempt to create a feeling of mutual trust and respect with staff.

Economic rewards – Ensuring the appropriate grading and pay for the duties and responsibilities undertaken by staff. Opportunities for improving skills, knowledge and promotion within a defined laboratory and career structure.

The extent of the commitment staff have to the laboratory will have a major influence in the level of work performance. Commitment can be defined as 'the relative strength of the employee's identification with, and involvement in any organisation'. This initiates a sense of loyalty, involvement and belief in the values of the organisation. This was highlighted in the studies of private sector companies.[6] A sense of belonging to the company built upon loyalty was seen as an essential part of industrial relations.

The sense of belonging was created by managers through ensuring that the workforce was:

- informed
- involved
- sharing the success of the company

Motivated through:

- trust
- pride
- accountability for results

Respect and confidence in management through attention to:

- authority
- dedication
- competence

A large measure of the success of the companies studied

derives from the management of people and from creating a climate of commitment.

This also applies to laboratory staff. If, for example, they feel trusted, respected and valued they will make the effort to show it is warranted.

Commitment from staff not only improves the overall perform-ance of the laboratory, it also affects the successful implementation of change within the laboratory. It also ensures that the laboratory becomes a better place to work in.

Resistance to change

Despite the potential positive outcomes, change is often resisted at both the individual and the organisational level. Resistance to change, or the thought of the implications of the change, appears to be a common phenomenon. People are naturally wary of change. "Among many there is an uneasy mood – suspicion that change is out of control"[32]

Resistance to change can take many forms and it is often diffi-cult to pinpoint the exact reasons for resistance. The forces against change in work organisations include: ignoring the needs and expectations of people; when people have insufficient information about the nature of the change or if they do not perceive the need for change.

Fears may be expressed over such matters as employment levels, job security, de-skilling of work, loss of job satisfaction, salary, change to social structures and working conditions, loss of individual control over work and greater management control.

Some common reasons for individual resistance within dental laboratories include the following:

Selective perception – The staff's own perception of stimuli presents a unique picture or image of the 'real' world and can result in selective perception. This can lead to a biased view of a particular situation which fits most comfortably into a person's own perception of reality, and this can cause resistance to change. For example, management may have been stereotyped as being untrustworthy, which will result in opposition to any proposed change.

Habit – Staff tend to respond to situations in an established and accustomed manner. Habits may serve as a means of comfort and security and as a guide for easy decision making.

Inconvenience or loss of freedom – If the change is seen as likely to prove inconvenient, make life difficult, reduce freedom of action or result in increased control there will be resistance.

Economic implications – Staff are likely to resist change which is perceived as reducing their pay either directly or indirectly, is requiring them to produce an increase in work for the same level of pay or is acting as a threat to their job security. This was highlighted in the study of hospital dental laboratories where staff had established grades and patterns of work and a vested interest in maintaining the status quo.[6]

Security in the past – There is a tendency for some staff to find a sense of security in the past. In times of frustration or difficulty, or when faced with new or unfamiliar ideas or methods, they may reflect in the past. There is a wish to retain the old comfortable ways. For example, placing faith in well established ('tried and trusted') procedures and clinging to these for a feeling of security.

Fear of the unknown – Changes which confront staff with the unknown tend to cause anxiety or fear. Major changes in a working environment present a degree of uncertainty. For example, the introduction of new technology or methods of working, or, a member of staff may resist promotion because of uncertainty over the changes in responsibilities and increased demands of the higher position.

Chapter 9 – Key points

- Strategic success requires leadership and managers with an ability to manage change and develop a culture which is responsive to perpetual change. It is important for managers to adopt a clearly defined strategy for the initiation of change, including attention to the style of leadership/management.
- Laboratory managers should monitor and review all aspects of the strategic plan at frequent intervals and adjust as necessary.
- Managers should recognise the importance of the people within the laboratory and make efficient use of human resources.
- The objective of appraisal is to improve the performance of staff leading to improvement in the efficiency and service of the laboratory. An effective appraisal system offers a number of potential benefits to both the individual and the laboratory.
- Despite the potential positive outcomes, change is often resisted by staff. People are naturally wary of change and resistance can take many forms and is often difficult to pinpoint. Ignoring the needs and expectations of staff and lack of information about the nature of the change are common reasons for resistance.
- The culture of the laboratory develops over time and may not be easy to change. An ineffective culture may result in a lack of flexibility for, or acceptance of, change.
- There should be full and genuine participation of all staff concerned before and during the change process.
- Climate is based on the perception of staff towards the laboratory and influences their attitude toward work and their colleagues. A healthy climate is an important factor in ensuring the laboratory provides an efficient and effective service to its customers. The introduction of incentive schemes may help in improving morale and motivating staff.
- To improve morale laboratory managers should review the main areas in which to develop the best possible attitudes in their staff.
- People are naturally wary of change. Resistance to change can take many forms and it is often difficult to pinpoint the exact reasons.

SUMMARY

The implementation of strategic change remains one of the most difficult areas of management. Success depends both on the selection of an appropriate strategy and converting that strategy into action. If either of these aspects is deficient the strategy may fail or be less effective than it should be, but often it is difficult after the event to know what went wrong.

Although much has been written on change management and transformational leadership, both of which are very relevant to strategy implementation, there has been nothing in the literature that has looked specifically at the process of implementing strategic change in dental laboratories.

The underlying theme of this book has been the methods and their effectiveness in the planning and implementation of strategic change, and the role of management as an integrated activity.

The author has endeavoured to provide a clear awareness and understanding of the problems of managing strategic change and a framework which offers defined models and proactive approaches for tackling the different scenarios commercial and hospital dental laboratory managers face when planning and implementing effective change. It is aimed at providing a useful insight into some of the ways in which managers should contribute to the process of change. It has examined, through the review of the relevant literature and use of case studies, techniques of analysis, evaluation and planning which can help the laboratory manager understand the process of strategic change.

The literature review and case studies undertaken by the author on strategic change, and management of the change processes, provide a linkage which has brought together a number of managerial approaches to implementation. More importantly it has stressed that it is the process of management i.e. the skills of managers, the ability to relate to their external environment, their internal culture and the people around them that will ensure success.

The book has concentrated on identifying a number of key theories, concepts and models for introducing, and implementing, change management and human resource strategies within a dental laboratory, their linkage to its business strategy (service to customers) and the factors affecting the successful implementation of change.

It provides both an understanding of management behaviour and the internal and external forces that can influence dental laboratory managers and how a laboratory's vision influences the change strategy, which in turn influences the choices made in selecting human resource strategies and policies. It has also shown that there is a critical need for such an integrated view of how different areas of strategic choice relate to each other.

The need for employee support and commitment has been shown to be essential to the success of the change process and the efficient delivery of the quality and standard of service customers demand. Importantly, it has highlighted that achieving strategic success is dependent upon aspects of both strategy and structure which in turn depend on effective strategic leadership.

A sound, appropriate, communicated and shared purpose and vision should be manifested in appropriate, feasible and desirable laboratory strategies. These must be implemented with a high level of customer service, continuous improvement and the ability to change to meet customer demand.

REFERENCES

1 Upton T, Brooks B. *Managing Change in the NHS*. Kogan Page, London, 1995

2 Glynn J, Perkins D. *Managing Healthcare*. W. B. Saunders, London, 1995

3 *The New NHS, Modern-Dependable*. The Stationary Office Limited. London, 1997, CM3807

4 *Summary Business Plan*. The Central Sheffield University Hospitals. 1998 – 99

5 Lee K. *The effect that reorganisation and funding constraints within the National Health Service have had on dental technology services*. MPhil Thesis, University of Sheffield,1997

6 Lee K. *The process of managing strategic change within a hospital dental laboratory*. PhD Thesis, University of Sheffield, 2000

7 Thompson J L. *Strategy in Action*, Chapman & Hall, London 1995

8 Burnes B. *Managing Change*, Pitman Publishing, London 1996

9 Johnson G, Scholes K. *Exploring Corporate Strategy*, Prentice Hall, London 1993

10 Thompson J L. *Lead with Vision: Manage the Strategic Change*, International Thomson Business Press, London 1997

11 Porter ME. *Competitive Advantage*, In *Creating and Sustaining Superior Performance*, Free Press, 1985

12 Pascal RT. Paper presented at *the Strategic Rennaissance Conference*, Strategic Planning Society, London October 1992

13 Senge P. *The Fifth Discipline*. In *The Art and Practice of the Learning Organisation*, City Business, London, 1990

14 Buchanan DA, Huczynski A A. *Organisational Behaviour*, Prentice-Hall International (UK) Ltd., London, 1985

15 Georgiades N, Macdonell R. *Leadership for Competitive Advantage,* John Wiley & Sons, Chichester, England, 1998

16 Zaleznik A. *Managers and Leaders: are they Different?* Harvard Business Review, May – June 1977

17 Burns JM. *Leadership*, Harper and Row, New York 1978

18 Hannagan T. *The Challenge of Management.* In *Management, Concepts and Practices.* Pitman Publishing, London 1995

19 Massie JL, Douglas J. *Managing a Contemporary Introduction,* Englewood Cliffs, Prentice Hall, New Jersey 1977

20 Weick K, *Letters to the editor*, Fortune, P27, October 17 1997

21 Kilman *et al*, *Gaining Control of the Corporate Culture*, Jossey – Bass, San Francisco CA 1988

22 Armstrong M. *Management Process and Functions*, Institute of Personnel Management, Short Run Press, Exeter 1990

23 Mintzeberg H. *The Nature of Managerial Work*, Harper and Row, New York 1973

24 Hamel G. *Competing for the Future*, Economist Conference, London June 1994

25 Thompson J L. *Strategic Management, Awareness and Change*, International Thomson Business Press, London 1997

26 Reed R, Buckley MR. *Strategy in Action – Techniques for Implementing Strategy*, Long Range Planning, **21**(3), 1988

27 Child J. *Organisation: A Guide to Problems and Practice*, Harper and Row, 2nd edition, London 1984

28 Drucker PF. *"New Templates for Today's Organisations"*, Harvard Business Review, PP 45-65, January – Febuary 1974

29 Hannagan T. *Management Control.* In *Management Concepts and Practices.* Pitman, London, 1995

30 PA Consultants. *How to Take Part in the Quality Revolution – A Management Guide*, Dr Steve Smith, PA Management Consultants 1987

31 Peters TJ. *Thriving in Chaos*, Macmillan, London, 1988

32 Thomas M. *What You Need to Know about Business Process Re-engineering.* In *Personnel Management.* P31, January 1994

GLOSSARY OF STRATEGIC MANAGEMENT TERMS

Acquisition: The purchase of one company by another, either for cash or equity in the parent. Sometimes the word *takeover* is preferred when the acquisition is hostile, and resisted by the company being bought. Similarly *mergers* are when two companies simply *agree* to come together as one.

Adaptive strategic change: Strategies which emerge and develop on an on-going basis as companies learn of new environmental opportunities and threats and adapt (or respond) to competitive pressures.

Adding value: Technically the difference between the value of a firm's outputs and its inputs; the additional value is added through the deployment and effort of the organisation's resources. Successful organisations will seek to add value to create outputs which are perceived as important by their customers. The *added value or supply chain* is the sequential set of activities from suppliers, through manufacturers and distributors which is required to bring products and services to the marketplace.

Alliance (strategic alliance): An agreement, preferably formalised, with another organisation. The alliance might be with an important supplier, with a major distributor, or possibly with a competitor, say for joint research and development.

Architecture: A relational network involving either or both external linkages (see strategic alliance) or internal linkages between managers in a company or businesses in a conglomerate. The supply chain is one such network. The main benefits concern information exchanges for the mutual gain of those involved, and synergies from interdependencies.

Benchmarking: A process of comparative evaluation – of products, services and the performances of equipment and personnel. Sometimes companies attempt to benchmark their competitors; on other occasions they will benchmark those organizations which are seen as high performers.

Business plan: A detailed plan setting out the objectives of a business over a stated period, often three, five or ten years. For a group of companies the business plan is often called a *corporate plan*.

Business process re-engineering: The analysis and re-design of workflows and processes within organisations and between them (i.e. along the supply chain).

Budgetary control: The process by which financial control is exercised within an organisation using budgets for income and expenditure for each function of the organisation in advance of an accounting period.

Cash flow: The amount of cash being received and expended by a business which is often analysed into its various components.

Change options matrix: This links the areas of human resource activity with the three main areas of strategic change: work, cultural and political change.

Changeability of the environment: The degree which the environment is likely to change.

Clinical governance: Describes the things the organisation does and uses to help measure and continuously improve its clinical services.

Competitive advantage: The ability of an organisation to add more value for its customers than its rivals, and thus attain a position of relative advantage. The challenge is to sustain any advantage once achieved.

Competitive analysis: The process of identifying the organisations key competitors and assessing their objectives, strategies, strengths and weaknesses as well as their likely reaction patterns.

Competitive strategy: The means by which organisations seek to achieve and sustain competitive advantage. Usually the result of distinctive *functional strategies*. There should be a competitive strategy for every product and service produced by the company.

Competitor profiling: Explores one or two leading competitors by analysing their resources performance, current products and strategies.

Complementors: The companies whose products add more value to the products of the base organisation than they would desire from their own products by themselves.

Controls: The process of monitoring the proposed plans as they are implemented and adjusting for any variances where necessary.

Co-operation: The links that bring organisations together, thereby enhancing their ability to compete in the market place. See also: **Complementors**.

Core competencies: The distinctive group of skills and technologies that enable an organisation to provide particular benefits to customers and deliver competitive advantage. Together, they form key resources of the organisation that assist it in being distinct from its competitors. See also: **Strategic capability**.

Core resources: The important strategic resources of the organisation, usually summarised as architecture reputation and innovation.

Corporate strategy: The pattern of major objectives, purposes or goals and the essential policies or plans for achieving those goals. Note that this is not the only definition i.e:

The overall strategy for a diversified or multi-product/multi-service organisation. Refers to the overall scope of the business in terms of products, services and geography.

Cost effectiveness Achieving a goal with the minimum of expenditure.

Cost/benefit analysis: Evaluates strategic projects especially in the public sector where an element of unquantified public service beyond commercial profit it may be involved. It attempts to quantify the broader social benefits to be derived from particular strategic initiatives, of capital.

Cost leadership: The lowest cost producer in a market – after adjustments for quality differences. An important source of competitive advantage in either a market or a segment of a market. Specifically the cost leader is the company which enjoys a cost advantage over its rivals through the management of its resources, and not because it produces the lowest quality.

Cost-plus pricing: Sets the price of goods and services primarily by totalling the costs and adding a percentage profit margin.

Cultural web: The factors that can be used to characterise the culture of an organisation. Usually summarised as stories, symbols, power structures, organisational structure, control systems, routines and rituals.

Culture: The values and norms of an organisation, which determine its corporate behaviour and the behaviour of people within the organisation.

Customer-driven strategy: The strategy of an organisation where every function is directed towards customer satisfaction. It goes beyond those functions, such as sales and marketing, that have traditionally had direct contact with the customer.

Customer profiling: Describes the main characteristics of the customer and how customers make their purchase decisions.

Decentralisation/centralisation: The extent to which authority, responsibility and accountability is devolved throughout the organisation. Centralisation should yield tight control; decentralisation motivates managers and allows for speedier reactions to environmental change pressures.

Delayering: The removal of layers of management and administration in an organisation's structure.

Demerger: The split of an organisation into its constituent parts with some parts possibly being sold to outside investors.

Differentiation: Products and services are differentiated when customers perceive them to have distinctive properties which set them apart from their competitors.

Diversification: The extent of the differences between the various products and services in a company's portfolio (its range of activities). The products and services may be related through say marketing or technology, or *unrelated*, which normally implies they require different management skills.

Divisionalisation: A form of organisation structure whereby activities are divided and separated on the basis of different products or services, or geographic territories.

Downsizing: A reduction in the size of an organisation especially by reducing the number of employees in order to save costs and increase the flexibility and adaptability of the organisation.

Economies of scale: The extra cost savings that occur when higher volume production allows unit costs to be reduced.

Effectiveness: The ability of an organisation to meet the demands and expectations of its various stakeholders, those individuals or groups with influence over the business. Sometimes known as 'doing the right things'.

Efficiency: The sound management of resources to maximise the returns from them. Sometimes known as 'doing things right'.

Emergent change: The whole process of developing a strategy whose outcome only emerges as the strategy proceeds. There is no defined list of implementation actions in advance of the strategy emerging. See also: **Prescriptive change**.

Empowerment: Freeing people from a rigid regime of rules, controls and directives and-allowing them to take responsibility for their own decisions and actions.

Environment: Everything and everyone outside the organisation: competitors, customers, government, etc. Note that 'green' environmental issues are only one part of the overall definition. See also: **Changeability of environment and Predictability of the environment.**

Entrepreneurial/visionary strategies: Strategies created by strong, visionary strategic leaders. Their successful implementation relies on an ability to persuade others their merit.

E-V-R Congruence: The effective matching of an organisation's resources (R) with demands of its environment (E). A successful and sustained match has to be managed and frequently requires change; successfully achieving this depends on the organisation's culture and values (V).

Focus strategy: Concentration on one or a limited number of market segments or niches.

Formal organisational structures: Those structures formally defined by the organisation in terms of reporting relationships, responsibilities and tasks. See also: **Informal organisational structures**.

Functional strategy: The strategy for the various functions carried out by an organisation, including marketing, production, financial management, information management, research and development, human resource management. One or more functional strategies will typically be responsible for any distinctive competitive edge company enjoys.

Gap analysis: A method of determining any difference between a firms objectives and what it will achieve in the future if it makes no changes to it strategy. See also: **Planning gap**.

Governance: The location of power and responsibility at the head of an organisation.

Holding company: A structure where the various businesses are seen as largely independent of each other and managed accordingly

Horizontal integration: The acquisition or merger of firms at the same stage in the supply chain. Such firms may be direct competitors or focus on different market segments.

Human resource-based theories of strategy: Emphasise the importance of the people element in strategy development. See also: **Emergent strategy.**

Implementation: The process by which the organisation's chosen strategies are put into operation.

Incremental strategic change: Changes to intended (possibly planned) strategies as are implemented. Results from on-going learning and from changes in the environment or to forecast assumptions.

Informal organisational structures: Those structures, often unwritten, that have been developed by the history, culture and individuals in an organisation to facilitate the flow of information and allocate power within the structure.

Innovation: Changes to products, processes and services in an attempt to sharpen their competitiveness through either cost reduction or improved distinctiveness. *Strategically it can apply to any part of a business.*

Intangible resources: The organisation's resources that have no physical presence but represent real benefit to the organisation like reputation and technical knowledge.

Internal growth (organic growth): The means by which a business can grow using its own resources i.e. product development.

Joint venture: A form of strategic alliance where each partner takes a financial stake. This could be a shareholding in the other partner or the establishment of a separate, jointly-owned, business.

Just in time: An approach to manufacturing that aims to reduce waste. It seeks to improve all performance variables such as cost quality speed dependability and flexibility.

Key (or critical) success factors: Environmentally based factors which are crucial for competitive success. Simply the things an organisation must be able to do well if it is to succeed.

Knowledge: A fluid mix of framed experience, values, contextual information and expert insight. Note that knowledge is not 'data' or 'information'.

Knowledge management: The retention, exploitation and sharing of knowledge in an organisation that will deliver sustainable competitive advantage.

Leadership: The art or process of influencing people so that they will strive willingly and enthusiastically towards the achievement of the group's mission.

Learning organisation: One which is capable of harnessing and spreading best practices, and where employees can learn from each other and from other organisations. The secret lies in open and effective communication networks.

Logistics: The science of stockholding, delivery and customer service.

Management: The running of an organisation or part of it. Management has two main components: an organisational skill including the ability to lead and delegate and an entrepreneurial sense.

Manager: They see their job as organising the resources and the people to ensure that goals are achieved.

Marketing: The process of planning and executing the conception, pricing, promotion and distribution of ideas, products and services to create exchanges that will satisfy the needs of individuals and organisations.

Market segmentation: The use of particular marketing strategies to target identified and defined groups of customers.

Minimum intervention: The principle that managers implementing strategy should only make changes where they are absolutely necessary.

Mission statement: A summary of the essential aim or purpose of the organisation's essential reason for being in business.

Net cash flow: Approximately, the sum of pre-tax profits plus depreciation, less the capital to be invested in a strategy.

Objective: A short-term target or milestone with defined measurable achievements. A desired state and hoped-for level of success.

Operating system: The configuration of activities concerned with transforming resources within an organisation. Each system is an attempt to achieve the optimum match between organisational capabilities and perceived environmental conditions.

Organisational capability: The skills, routines, management and leadership of its organisation.

Organisational politics: The process by which individuals and groups utilise power and influence to obtain results. Politics can be used legitimately in the best interests of the organisation, or illegitimately by people who put their own interests above those of the organisation.

Paradigm: The recipe or model that links the elements of a theory together and shows, where possible, the nature of the relationships.

Performance appraisal: An evaluation of the performance of an employee which may be used to decide an employee's pay, career prospect and training and development requirements.

Performance measures indicators: The key measures and subjective indicators of the performance of a company which are monitored and assessed to ensure its long term success. These indicators often pinpoint the strengths and weaknesses of the company and are often divided into: Strategic, operational, financial, behavioural, environmental and ethical.

Plans or programmes: The specific actions that follow from the strategies. Often a step-by-step sequence and timetable.

Planning gap: A planning technique which enables organisations to evaluate the potential for, and risk involved in, seeking to attain particular growth targets.

Policies: Guidelines relating to decisions and approaches which support organisational efforts to achieve stated objectives. They are basically guides to thoughts (about how things should be done) and actions.

Portfolio planning: Techniques for evaluating the appropriate strategies for a range of (possibly diverse) business activities in a single organisation.

Power: The potential or ability to do something or make something happen. Externally it refers to the ability of an organisation to influence and affect the actions of its external stakeholders. Internally it concerns the relationships between people.

Predictability of the environment: The degree to which changes in the environment can be predicted.

Prescriptive change: The implementation actions that result from the selected strategy option. A defined list of actions is identified once the strategy has been chosen. See also: **Emergent change**.

Profitability: The ratio of profits from a strategy divided by the capital employed in that strategy, it is important to define clearly the elements in the equation, e.g. whether the profits are calculated before or after tax and before or after interest payments. This is often called the Return On Capital Employed, shortened to ROCE.

Quality: Strategically quality is concerned with the ability of an organisation to 'do things right – first time and every time' for each customer. This includes internal customers (other departments in an organisation) as well as external customers. *Total Quality Management* is the spreading of quality consciousness throughout the whole organisation.

Reputation: The strategic standing of the organisation in the eyes of its customers.

Resource allocation: The process of allocating the resources of the organisation selectively between competing strategies according to their merit.

Resource-based view: Stresses the importance of resources in delivering the competitive advantage of the organisation

Reward: The result of successful strategy, adding value to the organisation and the individual.

Risk management: The understanding where and how things can and might go wrong, appreciating the extent of any downside if things do go wrong and putting in place strategies to deal with the risks either before or after they occur.

Scenario: A conceptual possibility of future events and circumstances. Scenario planning involves using these to explore what might happen in order to prepare managers for a wide range of eventualities and uncertainties in an unpredictable future.

Stakeholder: Any individual or group capable of affecting (and being affected by) the actions and performance of an organisation.

Strategy: The means by which organisations achieve (and seek to achieve) their objectives and purpose. There can be a strategy for each product and service, and for the organisation as a whole.

Strategic awareness: Appreciating the strategic position and relative success of the organisation. Knowing how well it is doing, why and how – relative to its competitors and appreciating the nature of the strategic environment and the extent of any need to change things.

Strategic business unit: A discrete grouping within an organisation with delegated responsibility for strategically managing a product, a service, or a particular group of products or services.

Strategic capability: Process skills used to add value and create competitive advantage.

Strategic change: Changes which take place over time to the strategies and objectives of the organisation. Change can be gradual, emergent and evolutionary, or discontinuous, dramatic and revolutionary

Strategic control: A style of corporate control whereby the organisation attempts to enjoy the benefits of delegation and decentralisation with a portfolio of activities which, while diverse, is interdependent and capable of yielding synergies from co-operation.

Strategic creation: Term for the formulation and choice of new strategies. Encapsulates direction from the strategic leader, strategic planning and emergent strategy.

Strategic fit: The matching process between strategy and organisational structure.

Strategic issues: Current and forthcoming developments inside and outside the organisation which will impact upon the ability of the organisation to pursue its mission and achieve its objectives.

Strategic leader: Generic term used to describe those managers who are responsible for changes in the corporate strategy.

Strategic life cycle: The notion that strategies (like products and services) have finite lives. After some period of time they will need improving, changing or replacing.

Strategic management: The process by which an organisation establishes its objectives, formulates actions (strategies) designed to meet these objectives in the desired timescale, implements the actions and assesses progress and results.

Strategic planning (*in strategy creation*): The systematic and formal creation of strategies – to be found in many organisations, and capable of making a very significant contribution in large, multi-activity organisations.

Strategic regeneration (or renewal): Major and simultaneous changes to strategies, structures and styles of management.

Stretching resources: The creative use of resources to add extra value for customers – through innovation and improved productivity.

Sustainable competitive advantage: An advantage over competitors that cannot be easily imitated. Such advantages will generate more value that competitors have.

Supply chain: The linkage between an organisation, its suppliers, distributers and its customers.

Style of leadership: Suggests that individuals can be identified who possess a general style of leadership that is appropriate to the organisation.

SWOT analysis: An analysis of an organisation's strengths and weaknesses alongside the opportunities and threats present in the external environment.

Synergy: The term used for the added value or additional benefits which ideally accrue from the linkage or fusion of two businesses, or from increased co-operation between either different parts of the same organisation or between a company and its suppliers, distributors and customers. Internal co-operation may represent linkages between either different divisions or different functions.

Tangible resources: The physical resources of the organisation like plant and equipment

Turnaround strategy: An attempt to find a new competitive position for a company in difficulty

Value chain: Identifies where the value is added in an organisation and links the process with the main functional parts of the organisation. It is used for developing competitive advantage because such chains tend to be unique to an organisation.

Value system: The wider routes in an industry that add value to incoming supplies and outgoing distributors and customers. It links the industry value chain to that of other industries. It is used for developing competitive advantage.

Vertical integration: Where companies directly enter those parts of the added value chain served by their suppliers or distributors, the term used is vertical integration. To achieve the potential benefits of vertical integration (specifically synergy from co-operation) without acquiring a business which normally requires specialist and different skills firms will look to establish strong alliances and networks.

Vision: A challenging and imaginative picture of the future role and objectives of an organisation, significantly going beyond its current environment and competitive position. It is often associated with an outstanding leader of the organisation.

INDEX